A SHORT HISTORY OF
THE SCOTTISH COAL-MINING INDUSTRY

ROTHES COLLIERY.

A SHORT HISTORY

OF THE

SCOTTISH COAL-MINING

INDUSTRY

PUBLISHED BY

THE NATIONAL COAL BOARD

SCOTTISH DIVISION

1st *Impression*
SEPTEMBER 1958

PRINTED BY
PILLANS & WILSON LTD.
EDINBURGH AND GLASGOW

CONTENTS

	Page
INTRODUCTION—Summary of Contents—Acknowledgments	13
CHAPTER I—Our Coals and Coalfields	17
1. The Age of Forests	17
2. The Origin of Coal	19
3. The Carboniferous Period	23
4. Later History of our Coals	26
5. Our Coalfields To-day	29
CHAPTER II—The Story of the Scottish Coal-Mining Industry from the end of the twelfth century to the beginning of the eighteenth	34
1. The Earliest Records	34
2. Period 1300 to 1450	35
3. Period 1450 to 1550	39
4. Period 1550 to 1700	40
CHAPTER III—The Story of the Scottish Coal-Mining Industry during the eighteenth century and first half of the nineteenth	46
1. Period 1700 to 1750	46
2. Period 1750 to 1800	47
3. Period 1800 to 1850	50
CHAPTER IV—Conditions of Life and Work in early Scottish Coal Mines	55
CHAPTER V—The Story of Technical Progress in the Industry during the last Hundred Years	61
CHAPTER VI—The Industry Nationalised	85
CHAPTER VII—Mining Hazards and the Development of Safety Precautions	89
CHAPTER VIII—Types and Uses of Scottish Coals	101

LIST OF PLATES

FACING
PAGE

PLATE 1. A—Reconstruction of a scene in one of the Forest Swamps of Carboniferous times (for explanation see p. 12). B—Fossil Grove, Victoria Park, Whiteinch, Glasgow (for explanation see p. 12).   12

PLATE 2. Some characteristic plant and animal remains found in beds associated with our coal seams (for explanation see p. 12).   13

PLATE 3. Copy of an old engraving showing the great steam pumping-engine built by Claud Girdwood & Co. Glasgow, and erected at Newcraighall Colliery, Edinburgh, in 1828. The enormous cast-iron beam, receiving its motion from the 80-inch diameter piston of a double-acting steam cylinder, raised and lowered the shaft pump-rods through an 8-foot stroke thirteen times every minute. These rods, hanging in the shaft, operated pumps lifting the drainage water to the surface in several stages. Nothing now remains of the pumping-engine, but from the engraving it would appear to have been the largest of its type in Scotland.   52

PLATE 4. Photograph taken in 1886 of the remains of one of the earliest of Thomas Newcomen's atmospheric steam engines. Invented in 1711, these were at first applied to the work of pumping water from mines. They were introduced into Scotland about 1720.   53

PLATE 5. Beam engine made by Walkinshaw, Bridgeton, Glasgow, about 1790. Used as a winding engine at Dalry, Ayrshire, until 1875, and at Craigston Pit, Lugar, Ayrshire, until 1890. Thereafter, in service as a crab and haulage engine at Highhouse Colliery, Ayrshire, until 1956. The original crank and shaft were of cast iron and in one piece, with the valve gear being worked from the rocking beam.
    Presented to the Heriot-Watt College, Edinburgh, by the National Coal Board, November, 1957.   53

PLATE 6—WINDING DEVELOPMENTS. Electric winding engine at a Scottish colliery.   60

PLATE 7—MECHANICAL DECKING. Reconstructed surface showing the two transporters handling mine cars at the tipplers. Feed belt to washer in the foreground.   60

PLATE 8—JOY CONTINUOUS MINER.   61

PLATE 9—MODERN UNDERGROUND TRANSPORT. Diesel locomotive drawing train of mine cars.   61

PLATE 10—A.B. FIFTEEN LONG-WALL COAL-CUTTER, fitted with mushroom jib and arranged for flight-loading.   .   .   .   80

PLATE 11—MECO-MOORE CUTTER-LOADER.   80

PLATE 12—GARTSHERRIE MACHINE.   81

PLATE 13—NEW COLLIERIES. Killoch Colliery, near Ochiltree, Ayrshire, under construction.   88

PLATE 14—NEW COLLIERIES. An aerial view of the new Kinneil Colliery, Bo'ness, West Lothian.   88

PLATE 15—DRILLING FOR COAL AT SEA. Boring Tower in the Firth of Forth. The tower is resting on the seabed and the drilling rig is contained in the pyramid-shaped structure on the top deck.   (Backing Plates 13 & 14)

PLATE 16.   Operator removing section of the core from the bore pipe. .   .   .   .   (Do.)

PLATE 17—MINING MACHINERY. Coal plough at the coalface. .   (Backing Plates 19 & 20)

PLATE 18—MINING MACHINERY. Trepanner. Picture also includes "Roofmaster" self-advancing chocks and panzer conveyor.   .   .   .   .   (Do.)

PLATE 19—MINING MACHINERY. Long-wall coal-cutter at the coalface.   89

PLATE 20—ANDERTON SHEARER LOADER, showing the cutting head and plough attachment.   89

PLATE 21—SAFETY. Trainee being instructed in prop setting. .   96

PLATE 22—MINERS' LAMPS AND LIGHTING. *Left to right:*— 1. Spedding Mill (flint and steel, abt. 1760). 2. Wolf miniature oil lamp (modern). 3. Modern oil lamp used for gas testing. 4. Marsaut lamp (about 1882). 5. Marsaut type. 6. Stephenson lamp (early 1870's). 7. Clanny lamp (about 1839).   .   .   96

PLATE 23—SHOTFIRING. Testing for gas holding lamp close to roof.   97

PLATE 24—SHOTFIRING. Miner using an electrical drill prior to shotfiring.   97

LIST OF ILLUSTRATIONS

PAGE

FIGURE 1. Diagrammatic representation of a Forest-Swamp: for explanation see text, p. 19.　.　.　.　.　.　.　　18

FIGURE 2. Diagram to illustrate the invasion of a Forest-Swamp by the encroaching waters of an estuary or sea: see also text, p. 21.　.　.　.　.　.　.　.　.　.　　20

FIGURE 3. Diagram to illustrate the formation of a second Forest-Swamp: see text, p. 21.　.　.　.　.　.　.　　22

FIGURE 4. Diagram to illustrate conditions at the present day: 1. Lower Series of coals; 2. Upper Series of coals. At A a bore is being sunk to prove the Lower Series. At B the Upper Coals are being wrought by opencast methods, and at C the Lower Coals are being worked by shallow mines. At D deep shafts are working the Lower Coals and, in addition, one of the seams in the Upper Series. The area at the surface ornamented by dots and open circles indicates where the cover of loose, superficial deposits (see text, p. 29) is thickest.　.　.　.　.　.　.　.　　24

FIGURE 5. Sketch-map to show distribution of the principal coal-fields of Central Scotland.　.　.　.　.　.　.　　27

FIGURE 6. Table to show the major sub-divisions of the Carboniferous rocks of Scotland. Note the position of the Lower and Upper Series of coals.　.　.　.　.　.　　29

FIGURE 7. Diagrammatic Horizontal Section across portions of the Scottish coalfields, to show how the rocks have been folded and faulted.　.　.　.　.　.　.　.　.　.　　31

FIGURE 8. Diagram to illustrate early method of working coal at the outcrop. Here the coal is exposed on the sides of a river-gorge. Coal worked is shown by stippling; coal left unworked shown black.　.　.　.　.　.　.　.　.　.　　37

FIGURE 9. Diagrammatic representation of a Bell-Pit; see text, p. 37　.　.　.　.　.　.　.　.　.　.　　38

FIGURE 10. Diagram to illustrate early method of working shallow coals by the Pit-and-Adit System. Ornamentation as in Figure 8; drainage tunnel or day-level shown by arrows.　.　　38

FIGURE 11. Bearer: it was a common practice in the early days of the industry for the coal to be carried by women, known as bearers, from the working-face to the foot of the shaft. It was not until 1842 that the employment of women and children underground was forbidden by law. 40

FIGURE 12. Diagrammatic representation of a Stair-Pit: women were often employed not only to take the coal from the working-face to the foot of the shaft but also to carry their loads up ladders to the surface. A "load" might amount to 1½ hundredweights. . 41

FIGURE 13. Water-Gin: a machine formerly used for raising coal in shallow shafts; the wheel was operated by water. (From *A Glossary of Scotch Mining Terms*, by J. Barrowman, 1886.) . 43

FIGURE 14. Horse-Gin: a machine formerly used for raising coal in shallow shafts; it was operated by horse-labour, hence the terms horse-gin or horse-engine. (From *A Glossary of Scotch Mining Terms*, by J. Barrowman, 1886.) 43

FIGURE 15. Horizon Mining Layout. 64

FIGURE 16. Furnace Ventilation. 65

FIGURE 17. Axial Flow Fan. 66

FIGURE 18. Sirocco Fan. 67

FIGURE 19. Haulage Systems. 70

FIGURE 20. By-products of the manufacture of gas and coke from coal. 72-73

FIGURE 21. Koepe and Skip Winding Systems. . . . 78

EXPLANATION OF PLATE 1

A—Reconstruction of a scene in one of the Forest-Swamps of Carboniferous times.

Lepidodendron trees in central and right middle distance; *Calamites* in right foreground and extreme right. Tree-ferns and fern-like plants form undergrowth in the shade of the large trees.

Photograph of a Diorama in the Geological Survey Museum, London; reproduced by permission of the Director of the Geological Survey and Museum and of the Controller of H.M. Stationery Office.

B—Fossil Grove, Victoria Park, Whiteinch, Glasgow, showing stumps and forked roots of Scale-Trees (*Lepidodendron*). These fossil tree-stumps were discovered in 1882 and are preserved by Glasgow Corporation as a natural museum.

From a photograph in the collection of the Geological Survey and Museum, London; reproduced by permission of the Director of the Geological Survey and Museum and of the Controller of H.M. Stationery Office.

EXPLANATION OF PLATE 2

Some characteristic plant and animal remains found in beds associated with our coal-seams.

Figure 1, twice natural size; Figures 2 to 4, natural size; Figure 5, half natural size.

FIGURE 1—Part of frond of a fern-like plant belonging to a group of plants long since extinct, known as Pteridosperms. The specimen illustrated is *Sphenopteris obtusiloba* and comes from a boring in Nottinghamshire.

Photograph by courtesy of Professor J. Walton, Department of Botany, University of Glasgow.

FIGURE 2—A lamellibranch (" mussel ") shell from a boring in Ayrshire. These shells are often found in the beds of shale overlying coal seams. They lived for the most part in fresh water and for this reason are spoken of as non-marine lamellibranchs. There are many different forms, the one illustrated being known as *Anthracosia atra*.

Photograph by courtesy of Dr J. Weir, Department of Geology, University of Glasgow.

FIGURE 3—Piece of shale from a boring near Kilsyth, showing *Lingula* shells. *Lingula* is a common shell in our Carboniferous rocks. It had two equal valves loosely hinged together. The form illustrated is known as *Lingula mytiloides*.

Photograph by courtesy of Dr J. Weir.

FIGURE 4—Part of the outside of stem or branch of a Scale-tree (*Lepidodendron*) showing the characteristic leaf-scar pattern. The specimen comes from the shale (blaes) overlying the Main Coal at Argyll Colliery, Machrihanish, and is known as *Lepidodendron veltheimianum*.

Photograph by courtesy of Professor J. Walton.

FIGURE 5—Tooth of a large fish (*Rhizodus*) from the shale above a coal seam in a colliery near Bathgate.

Photograph by courtesy of Dr Ethel D. Currie, Hunterian Museum, University of Glasgow.

12

PLATE 1

A—Reconstruction of a scene in one of the Forest-Swamps of Carboniferous times. (For explanation see p. 12.)

B—Fossil Grove, Victoria Park, Whiteinch, Glasgow. (For explanation see p. 12.)

PLATE 2
Some characteristic plant and animal remains found in beds associated with our coal seams. (For explanation see p. 12)

INTRODUCTION
SUMMARY OF CONTENTS
ACKNOWLEDGMENTS

THE MAIN PURPOSE of this book is to provide a short history of the Scottish coal-mining industry, primarily for the use of senior pupils in schools. The story is prefaced by a brief account of our coals and coalfields. Much has yet to be learned about the origin of coal and about the chemical or physico-chemical processes by which the decomposed remains of vegetation were converted, in the course of incredibly long ages, into the material we now know under that name. The formation and subsequent history of our coals are the subject matter of Chapter I, but it is at best a fragmentary record and only the merest outline can be attempted here.

Succeeding chapters deal with the rise and development of coal-mining in Scotland and with the general economic background against which its story must be set. Nothing is known of the circumstances under which coal first came to be used in Scotland. The earliest records of its being actually worked date from the end of the twelfth and the beginning of the thirteenth centuries, but it must have been known, and its potential value realised to some extent at least, long before. In those early times there was plenty of timber available to meet the needs of a sparse and scattered population, while for such industries as required a more intense heat wood-charcoal[1] was available. Coal, perhaps first as pieces picked up near an outcrop on the sea-shore[2] or collected along the banks of streams, would only slowly come into use in districts where wood was becoming scarce.

So far as actual records exist, our story falls, broadly speaking, into two major and strongly contrasted periods of time. The first of these, extending from the end of the twelfth century to the middle of the eighteenth, was a period during which mining methods made, and indeed could make, little progress. It is true that they passed through various stages of development, from simple quarrying at an outcrop to the pit-and-adit system (p. 37), but only the shallowest seams could be worked—and even these only intermittently and on a small scale. Coal, we know, was wrought

---

[1] Wood-charcoal was made by the slow, partial combustion of cut wood built up into circular heaps.

[2] It was to coal obtained in this way that the term " sea-coal " was originally applied.

by the monks of some of the great abbeys during the thirteenth, fourteenth and fifteenth centuries. It was used also in the royal castles and in the mansions of the nobility, as well as for such industrial purposes as the manufacture of salt by the evaporation of sea-water in pans and the making of iron goods and ornamental ironwork. But there were a number of factors which together prevented its wider and more general use. In the first place it must be remembered that the centuries we are dealing with were a troubled and stormy period in Scottish history, a period which included the long War of Independence and the continued struggle to achieve a national unity. Throughout this period Scotland had only a small and scattered population, living for the most part under conditions of extreme poverty. A third factor was lack of means of communication, for while transport of coal and other goods by sea was possible in coastal areas, inland districts were served merely by rough tracks suitable only for pack-horses. Still another factor lay in the popular prejudice against the use of coal as a domestic fuel on account of the smoke and fumes given off. Indeed, it was not until the invention of proper fireplaces and chimneys[1] in the sixteenth century that this prejudice died away. Nevertheless, coal gradually replaced wood in households and also found expanding markets in such industries as the refining of metals, distilling, tanning, soap-making, etc. Even as late as 1700, however, the annual output of coal in Scotland was probably less than half a million tons.

The second major period in the history of coal-mining (see Chapter III) opened in the latter half of the eighteenth century when Scotland experienced a rapid and unprecedented expansion in industrial activities of all kinds, in agriculture and in overseas trade. These years were indeed a " golden age " in Scottish history, an age in which we find side by side with a striking advance in social and economic conditions a fresh, vigorous and entirely native intellectual renaissance. It was as if the Scottish spirit had been all at once set free and inspired to its greatest achievements.[2] It was

[1] The first type of chimney was simply a portable iron funnel which trapped the smoke and directed it up to the roof.

[2] The flowering of Scottish genius at this time showed itself in literature, philosophy, science and the arts; outstanding names are those of Burns (1759-96), Scott (1771-1832) and Galt (1779-1839) in literature; Hume (1711-76) in philosophy; Smith (1723-90) in political economy; Black (1728-99) and Hutton (1726-97) in science; Ramsay (1714-84), Adam (1728-92) and Raeburn (1756-1823) in the arts.

also an age of great discoveries and inventions, an age which witnessed, for example, the beginnings of the iron-making industry and the first use of coal-coke to smelt home ores. But the invention which far more than any other contributed to the rapid expansion of industry was that due to the genius of James Watt. By 1784 Watt had so far perfected his double-acting, rotary steam-engine (p. 48) that it could be employed to drive machinery of all kinds. The age of steam-power had arrived and the Industrial Revolution had begun. It was a revolution which, carried on with an increasing impetus into the nineteenth century, profoundly affected the whole economic structure and social life of the country. For the coal-mining industry the steam-engine meant a new lease of life. Steam-power was now available to deal with the age-long menace of mine-waters and to raise water (and coal) from greater depths than had been hitherto possible; underground workings could be extended and new fields of coal opened out.

With the coming of the nineteenth century new inventions and discoveries united to multiply the uses of coal enormously. Two of these may be mentioned here. The use of coal-gas as a general illuminant; and the application of steam-power to the " travelling engine " as the first locomotives were called, followed by the boom in railway construction, mainly between 1830 and 1840. The story of the mining industry during the crowded years of the first half of the century becomes one of constant endeavour to meet the growing demands of industry. Larger and larger supplies of coal were needed to feed the blast-furnaces, the gas-works, the steam-powered factories of the fast-growing industrial centres, the railways, the export markets and the first sea-going vessels to use steam instead of sail. The annual production of coal rose from an estimated figure of some 1,600,000 tons towards the end of the eighteenth century to one of about 17,000,000 tons by 1873.

It was also during the first half of the nineteenth century that the first important and long-delayed steps were taken to improve the lot of workers in coal-mines. Actually it was not until 1842 that the employment underground of women and girls and of boys below the age of ten was forbidden by law. Chapter IV of the book deals with the subject of life and work in the early Scottish coal-mines. Chapters V and VI continue the story of mining and give a résumé of the main lines along which progress has been made during the last hundred years. Chapter VII is devoted to an account of

15

the development of safety precautions to deal with the hazards of the miners' calling, while Chapter VIII describes briefly some aspects of the uses, marketing and distribution of coal.

The compilation and editing of the book have been undertaken on behalf of the Scottish Division of the National Coal Board by Mr James McKechnie and Dr Murray Macgregor. Dr Macgregor is responsible for Chapter I and has collaborated with Mr McKechnie in the preparation of Chapters II and III. Mr McKechnie contributes Chapters IV, VI and VII. Chapter V has been written by Mr McKechnie in collaboration with Mr James Lawrie and other members of the Production Department, while the information embodied in the later paragraphs of Chapter VIII was supplied by the Marketing Department of the Divisional Board.

Acknowledgments—The authors and publishers express their thanks to Mr R. H. Guild, Mr J. Hossack, Mr A. Dall and Miss E. Graham, members of the Text-book Committee of the Royal Scottish Geographical Society, for suggestions in regard to the scope and format of the book, which has, in fact, been prepared in response to a request from that body. Sir Andrew M. Bryan, LL.D., has supplied much valuable material and is due a special measure of thanks. Acknowledgment must also be made to various members of the Divisional Coal Board staff for their co-operation during the preparation of the book, and to the Controller of H.M. Stationery Office for permission to reproduce from official photographs the two illustrations facing page 12. The photographs of plant and animal remains appearing in Plate II were kindly supplied by the Botanical and Geological Departments of Glasgow University and individual acknowledgment of their source is made elsewhere.

Finally, to all who have in one way or another contributed to the compilation of this text-book the editors would like to extend their sincere thanks. They would specially wish to acknowldge the valuable assistance received from Mr R. L. Barrowman.

J. McK. and M.M.

CHAPTER I

OUR COALS AND COALFIELDS

AT FIRST GLANCE a lump of coal has the appearance of a black, brittle, dull or bright substance without any very definite structure. Careful inspection, however, shows that it is layered or stratified and that among the softer layers present it is possible to find pieces of flattened stems, twigs, leaves and roots. Thin sections of the harder bands, again, when examined under the microscope, reveal many scraps of plant-tissue, as well as other plant-remains such as the hard cases of spores, fragments of resin, etc. It is clear, accordingly, that coal must be regarded as an accumulation of vegetable debris which has in the course of long ages undergone decay, decomposition and compression to such an extent that only the more resistant portions of the original plant structures have been preserved. Its chemical composition also shows it to be of vegetable origin.

1. THE AGE OF FORESTS

The once living plants whose remains have gone to form our coals flourished in extensive forest-jungles and forest-swamps that covered much of what is now Scotland many millions of years ago when geographical and climatic conditions were very different from what they are to-day. It is for this reason that the period of geological time during which our coals were formed is sometimes spoken of as the Age of Forests. A modern parallel to these ancient forests and forest-swamps may be found in the mangrove-swamps of tropical countries. But it must be remembered that the plants of the " Coal-Forests " were very different from those growing at the present time. Many were of types that no longer exist. Some were tall trees, over a hundred feet in height,[1] whose closest allies to-day are the small club-mosses of our Scottish upland moors; others, with jointed, woody stems,[2] resembled our lowly horse-tails but were much larger and very abundant; others, again, the " Seed-Ferns", bore a foliage like that of our modern ferns, but belonged to

[1] Known as Scale-Trees (*Lepidodendron*) because the small leaves, when they fell off, left a pattern of scars on the stems and branches which gave them a scaly appearance; *see* Plate 1 and Plate 2, Figure 4.
[2] Known as *Calamites* (from the Latin *calamus*, a reed); *see* Plate 1A.

17

THE COAL FORESTS

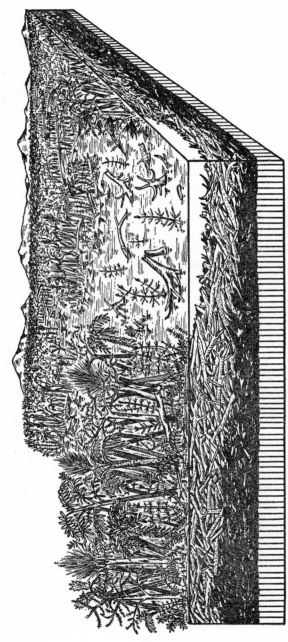

FIGURE 1. Diagrammatic representation of a Forest-Swamp: for explanation see text, p. 19.

an entirely different group of plants that has long since died out. The vegetation of the Coal-Forests was of an early, primitive type. There were no brightly-coloured flowering plants and none of the common trees of our woodlands to-day. Animal life also was represented by primitive types. The most highly-developed creatures of the forest-swamps were early salamander-like reptiles. There were no mammals and while insects were plentiful there were as yet no birds.

The illustration forming Plate 1A is a pictorial representation of a scene in a Coal-Forest. In this the various trees and other plants have been shown as they may well have appeared in that remote period of time when they actually grew; and if we wish to see a small corner of one of these ancient forests preserved in fossil form, we have only to visit the Fossil Grove at Victoria Park, Whiteinch, Glasgow (Plate 1B).

2. THE ORIGIN OF COAL

It was, then, in these old forests and forest-swamps that we find the beginning of the long story of our coals. There are, of course, many different seams of coal in Scotland (see, for example, the table on p. 32) and it must be realised that *each* of these seams represents a period of luxuriant forest-growth during which a rich vegetation of trees, tree-ferns, ferns and swamp-loving plants of all kinds covered wide tracts of land in a warm, humid climate. On the floors of the forests and in the shallow waters of the swamps, a tangled mass of decaying plant-remains—broken stems, roots, branches, twigs, leaves, etc.—slowly accumulated in a growing pile as successive generations of plants added their debris in turn. So that when we remember that *each* of these periods of forest-growth must in itself represent a long interval of time, amounting perhaps to thousands of years, we begin to realise something of the meaning and scale of geological time.

We have now to consider how it was that this mass of decaying vegetable matter came, in course of time, to be consolidated and slowly transformed into the material we know as coal. The following diagrams are intended to represent pictorially some of the early stages in this transformation.

Figure 1 shows a Coal-Forest with a rich vegetation of trees, etc. growing on the margins of a swamp. Plant-debris of all kinds is

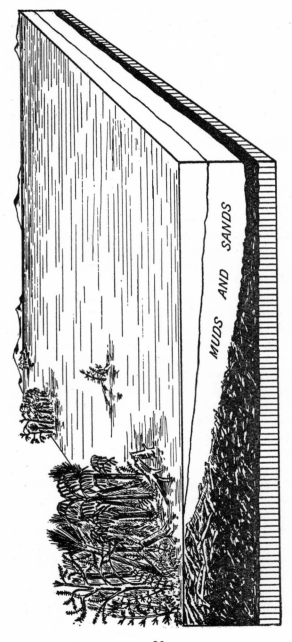

MUDS AND SANDS

FIGURE 2. Diagram to illustrate the invasion of a Forest-Swamp by the encroaching waters of an estuary or sea: see also text, p. 21.

collecting on the floor of the forest areas and in the shallow waters of the swamp. Through the forest sluggish rivers rising in the higher ground beyond meander slowly towards the coast, sometimes confined in channels, sometimes spreading out into broad stretches of swamp. Giant trees, reaching up to heights of over 100 feet, tree-ferns, ferns and tall " horse-tails " (*Calamites*) struggle for sunlight in steamy tropical heat.

These plants drew up water and chemicals from the soil in which they were anchored and their leaves extracted gases from the atmosphere. One of these gases was carbon dioxide (CO_2) and the green colouring matter of the leaves, in the presence of sunlight, provided the energy by which the plant was able to break up the carbon dioxide and utilise the carbon in the building up of the complex sugars and starches it required for its continued growth. It is the same process that goes on in our green plants to-day, and it is a fascinating thought to remember that when we burn coal we are warming ourselves with the sunshine of 250 million years ago.

As shown in the next Figure (Fig. 2) a rapid subsidence or depression of the land has taken place and allowed the waters of a shallow estuary or sea to invade the old forest area. Into this estuary or sea rivers from the surrounding high ground bring down muds and sands which gradually cover over and preserve the rotting vegetation of the forest floor. For thousands of years this process goes on and as more and more layers of mud and sand are deposited their increasing weight helps to compress and consolidate the sealed-up debris of the earlier forest and start it off on its transformation into coal.

A further stage is illustrated in Figure 3. Here we must imagine that many thousands of years have passed and gone. The depression over which the shallow waters of Figure 2 had spread has now been filled up with the incoming of muds and sands. When this happens a fresh land surface is formed and once again the forest reigns supreme. Once more trees and other plants live their lives and die and once again their remains accumulate to form a thick pile of tangled forest litter. And then, in course of time, another subsidence of the land takes place followed by a fresh invasion of the sea. This cycle of events, namely the alternation of periods of quiet, widespread forest-growth with periods of subsidence of the land, was repeated again and again and it is to this repeated alternation that we can

21

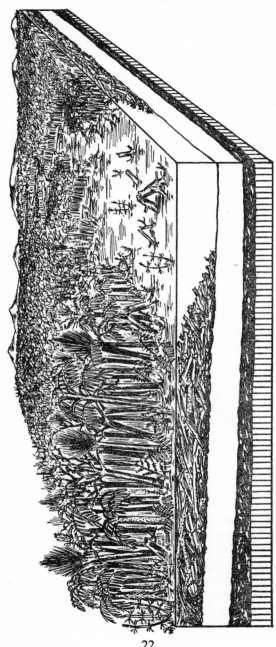

FIGURE 3. Diagram to illustrate the formation of a second Forest-Swamp: see text, p. 21.

trace back the origin of the successive coal-seams that are worked to-day in our coalfields.

3. THE CARBONIFEROUS PERIOD

So far in our story the period of time during which our coals were formed has been referred to as the Age of Forests. Geologists, however, from long usage, speak of it as the Carboniferous (that is, coal-bearing) Period. It must be remembered that the Carboniferous Period—only one of the major periods into which geological time is divided—was immensely long, lasting for some 60 million years. It must also be remembered that the particular conditions of geography and climate suitable for (a) the growth of extensive forests and (b) the preservation of their remains—conditions outlined in the previous paragraphs—were merely episodes in a long and complicated story. It is a story of constantly changing geological and geographical conditions and of widespread transformations of scenery and landscape. It is a story that we, at this distance of time, can only read in the succession of rocks of different kinds formed throughout Carboniferous times. The total thickness of these rocks in Scotland may be as much as 8,000 or 9,000 feet, almost twice the height of Ben Nevis. The story they tell us is one of repeated subsidences of the land and slow invasions of the sea. Our coal seams testify that there were recurring intervals when, in the tropical forest-swamps, plant-remains accumulated to a varying but considerable depth. Subsidence of the land led to the drowning of the forests by the encroaching waters first of shallow estuaries and finally of the open seas. And then, in course of ages, the seas themselves shallowed and their depressions were filled by the waste material brought down by rivers from the surrounding hills.

The commonest types of rocks that occur are sandstones and shales, originally the coarser and finer materials carried down in this way into the lagoons, estuaries and seas of Carboniferous times. In the seas themselves flourished a rich animal life and the shelly muds and layers of shelly debris which collected on the sea-floors formed in course of time the limestones that we find among our Carboniferous rocks to-day. From the evidence of the many shafts and borings (some of the latter over 4,000 feet deep) we now have a very complete knowledge of how this thick pile of Carboniferous rocks is built up and of the order in which the various

23

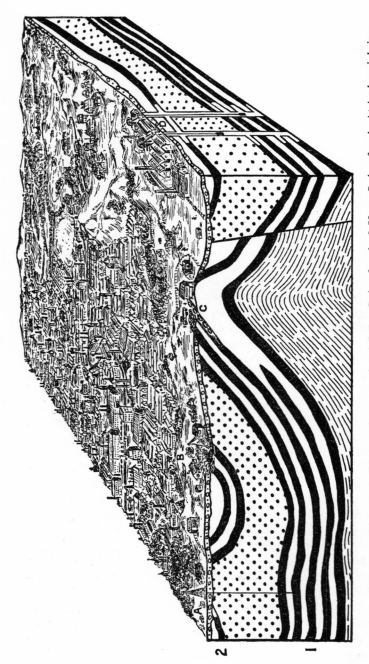

FIGURE 4. Diagram to illustrate conditions at the present day: 1. Lower Series of coals; 2. Upper Series of coals. At A a bore is being sunk to prove the Lower Series. At B the Upper Coals are being wrought by opencast methods, and at C the Lower Coals are being worked by shallow mines. At D deep shafts are working the Lower Coals and, in addition, one of the seams in the Upper Series. The area at the surface ornamented by dots and open circles indicates where the cover of loose, superficial deposits (see text p. 29) is thickest.

rock-types follow one another from the oldest to the youngest. These types include sediments originally laid down in seas, in estuaries, in land-locked lagoons, in river flood-plains and deltas, and upon the land itself, but now compacted and compressed into solid rocks. They include our sandstones, shales, limestones (both marine and fresh-water), coals, fireclays or underseats (representing the old soils of the Carboniferous forests), ironstones, etc. One other rock-type which has no relation as regards formation to the above, must be mentioned. These are the volcanic rocks represented by often extensive spreads of lavas and ashes poured or blown out of volcanoes which were active in many parts of what is now our Scottish Lowlands throughout the early part of Carboniferous times. These volcanic rocks to-day form the Campsie and Kilpatrick Hills, the upland ground between Renfrewshire and Ayrshire, the Garleton Hills of East Lothian, the Saline Hills in Fife, etc.

The thick succession of Carboniferous rocks can be broken up into a number of sub-divisions, each with its special characteristics and physical properties, and each representing a protracted portion of the whole Carboniferous Period. The names in use for these sub-divisions are given later. Here, however, it must be emphasised that in only two of these sub-divisions do coals play an important role. We have, accordingly, in Scotland two series of coal-bearing rocks separated by a great thickness of strata in which coals are relatively few.

Two important questions may be referred to at this point: (a) when did the piles of decaying vegetation that collected on the floors of the old forest-swamps become altered to the hard, brittle substance we know as coal; and (b) what were the agencies by which this alteration was brought about? As regards the first question there is evidence to show that the conversion of the parent-material to coal actually took place during Carboniferous times. The second question, however, cannot be answered except in very general terms. The conversion into coal was controlled initially by the extent and nature of the decomposition set up in the original plant debris by the action of bacteria and other organisms. This resulted in the formation of a kind of vegetable mould or humus in which only the more resistant portions of the plant substance was preserved. A second stage was reached when this mould or humus was buried under an increasing load of sediments, *i.e.*, sands and muds which in course of time became sandstones and shales. This increasing pressure led to compaction or consolidation of the humus, to a gradual loss in pore space, in moisture-content and in oxygen, and in the end to an increase in density, in carbon-content and in heat value.

4. LATER HISTORY OF OUR COALS

The Carboniferous Period came to an end some 200 odd million years ago and for most of this immensely long interval of time our coals and the whole series of rocks associated with them have lain buried and concealed. What happened to them during these 200 odd million years can only be dimly realised or guessed at. We know, however, that soon after the close of Carboniferous times a series of powerful earth-movements took place which compressed and folded the rocks so that the originally flat-lying beds of sandstone, shale, limestone, coal, etc., were tilted and inclined. A small-scale parallel to these effects may be obtained if a tablecloth is thrown into wrinkles and ridges by pressure on its ends. In much the same way the enormously powerful earth-movements compressed and elevated the Carboniferous rocks and folded them into a series of arches and basins. Another result was that, during the folding-movements, fractures or dislocations were set up along which the rocks on one side of the fracture slipped down or were displaced relatively to those on the other side. Such fractures are known as *faults* and as they are very common in our coalfields, where they vary in size[1] from a few feet up to hundreds of feet, they are a constant source of trouble in mining. The effects of folding and faulting of the Carboniferous rocks are diagrammatically represented in Figure 4.[2]

We know also that the same period of geological time which witnessed these folding movements in the crust of the earth, saw the invasion of the Carboniferous rocks by molten material from below. This molten material made its way upwards along fissures or fractures and solidified as more or less vertical walls of solid rock, or dykes as they are called. Where these dykes cut across coal-seams we find that they have burnt and destroyed the coal for a varying distance on either side. More serious results occur when the hot

---

[1] That is, in the relative amount of displacement of the rocks on the two sides of a fault.

[2] They are also illustrated in Figure 7.

molten material from depth has spread out laterally in the form of sheets or sills. If such a sheet follows a coal-seam closely it may render considerable areas of it useless by driving off the volatile constituents and leaving behind a cindery mass.

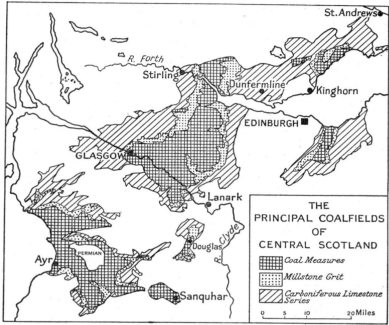

FIGURE 5. Sketch-map to show distribution of the principal coalfields of Central Scotland.

The interval that has elapsed since these events took place is about four times longer than the Carboniferous Period itself. In this interval many revolutions in earth-history have occurred and many widespread changes in the relative distribution of land and sea. To what extent our Scottish coalfield areas were involved in these changes it is not possible to say. The next great geological period to follow on the Carboniferous was the Permian, represented in Scotland mainly by a thick series of red sandstones, whose wind-rounded and polished sand-grains and other characteristics show that they were the product of wind-action in extensive deserts. Some of these red sandstones overlie the Carboniferous rocks in Central Ayrshire, as shown on Figures 5 and 7, and they may well

27

at one time have covered and concealed our coalfield areas everywhere. Whether they were themselves covered by deposits of later geological periods we do not know.[1] What we do know, however, is that for the last 60 million years or so Scotland has been in the main a land-area and as such subjected to the slow processes of erosion and denudation. Vast quantities of rock-material have been bit by bit removed and carried away by rivers and the whole land-area slowly and gradually reduced nearer and nearer to sea level. In course of time the overlying rocks were largely stripped off and the long-buried Carboniferous rocks with their included coals laid bare. These Carboniferous rocks were in turn subjected to erosion and where the old folding movements had thrown them into arches and basins it was the former that were now attacked. These were cut down and levelled off with the result that it was only in the basin-shaped structures that the coal-bearing rocks were preserved.

The last of the geological time-periods to which a brief reference must be made was the Glacial Period or Ice Age as it is sometimes termed. It began about a million years ago with a gradual onset of colder and colder conditions, until in the course of many hundreds of years the temperature fell so low that high-level ice fields and glaciers were formed. Finally, as Arctic conditions grew more intense, Scotland was covered with a slowly moving ice-sheet many hundreds of feet thick.[2] The Glacial Period came to an end some 25,000 years ago and in its closing stages all the conditions that marked its beginning took place in reverse order. The great ice-sheet gradually broke up and gave way in time to valley glaciers which disappeared in their turn as the climate slowly grew milder and milder.

It is because the Glacial Period occurred so recently (geologically speaking) that its effects are still to be clearly seen. The great ice-sheet, moving slowly outwards across the country from the higher ground, carried with it and under it vast quantities of broken and ground-up rock material. On the retreat and final disappearance of the ice all this carried material was left behind as an irregular hum-

---

[1] The geological periods, each representing a vast interval of time, which followed the Permian were the Triassic, the Jurassic and the Cretaceous. The coal worked at Brora on the East Sutherland coast is of Jurassic age and therefore very much younger than the coals of central Scotland.

[2] The Scottish ice-sheet was only a small part of an immense sheet which covered most of the Northern Hemisphere.

mocky blanket or mantle of rock fragments and debris, sometimes in the form of broad stretches of stiff clay full of boulders of all shapes and sizes, sometimes in the forms of spreads of sand and gravel. This mantle of glacial deposits of different kinds, known collectively as " drift", covers over and conceals most of our coalfield areas, and since it consists of more or less loose and unconsolidated material, it may in places be a source of danger where shallow workings are in progress.

5. OUR COALFIELDS TO-DAY

The conditions as we find them to-day are illustrated diagrammatically in Figure 4. In this figure the lower series of coals are shown as folded into an arch, the top of which has been eroded away at C. The coals come to the surface, or outcrop, on this arch and are represented as being worked by opencast (quarrying) methods or by shallow mines. The same coals are also reached by deep vertical shafts at D. The upper series of coals are shown as present only in shallow basins and one of them is being wrought from the same shafts as the lower series. While this figure indicates,

MAJOR SUB-DIVISIONS OF
THE SCOTTISH CARBONIFEROUS ROCKS

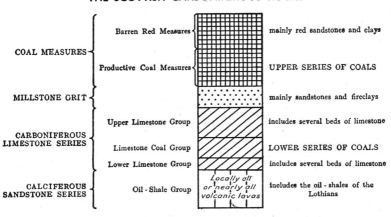

FIGURE 6.   Table to show the major sub-divisions of the Carboniferous rocks of Scotland. Note the position of the Lower and Upper Series of coals.

in a very general way, the conditions in some parts of our coal-fields, in other areas again all the upper series of coals as well as the lower series are present.

In an earlier paragraph (p. 25) reference was made to the fact that the Carboniferous rocks fall into a number of sub-divisions, each with its own special characteristics. These sub-divisions are shown in Figure 6 from which it will be seen that the " upper series " of coals corresponds with the Productive Coal Measures of the figure and the " lower series " with the Limestone Coal Group. The names Productive Coal Measures and Limestone Coal Group are now in general use for the two groups of rocks in which most of our valuable coal-seams occur.

The map forming Figure 5 shows the distribution of the principal coalfields of Scotland. From this, however, the following coalfield areas are omitted:—

(1) The Machrihanish field on the west coast of Kintyre, where one of the coals in the Limestone Coal Group is at present being worked.

(2) The Canonbie field on the Scottish Borders, south of Langholm, Dumfriesshire, last worked in 1922. An important extension of this field of Productive Coal Measures underneath a cover of later rocks has recently been proved by borings put down by the National Coal Board.

(3) The little field of coal at Brora, on the East Sutherland coast. The coal worked is of Jurassic age.

The map shows that the main coalfields occur in more or less separate basin-shaped areas. For example, the centre of the Midlothian Basin (see Fig. 7a) is occupied by Coal Measures, with the Limestone Coal Group, the central sub-division of the Carboniferous Limestone Series, underlying them in depth and rising to the surface on the margins of the basin. Thus a shaft at Loanhead or at Newtongrange will cut only the lower coals, while a shaft in the centre of the basin, such as that now being sunk at Monktonhall, between Musselburgh and Dalkeith, will penetrate both series.

Figure 7 illustrates the structure of some of our basin-shaped coalfields by means of three horizontal sections drawn across (a) Midlothian, (b) East Fife, and (c) Central Ayrshire. These sections are made up by taking the depths to particular beds, such as coals, limestones, etc., as proved in borings and shafts, and in this way obtaining a picture of the shape of the coalfield and of

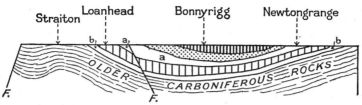

Straiton   Loanhead   Bonnyrigg   Newtongrange

(a) *Section across the Midlothian Coalfield*
(Distance about 5½ miles)

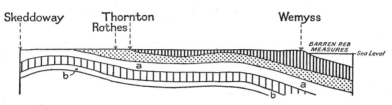

Skeddoway   Thornton   Wemyss
            Rothes

BARREN RED MEASURES
Sea Level

(b) *Section across the East Fife Coalfield*
(Distance about 5 miles)

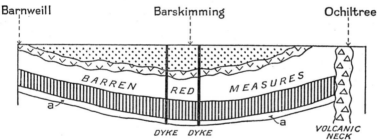

Barnweill   Barskimming   Ochiltree

BARREN RED MEASURES

DYKE   DYKE   VOLCANIC NECK

(c) *Section across Central Ayrshire (Mauchline Basin)*
(Distance about 8 miles)

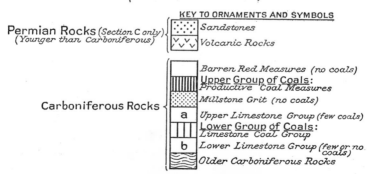

KEY TO ORNAMENTS AND SYMBOLS

Permian Rocks (Section C only)
(Younger than Carboniferous)

:::::: *Sandstones*

v v v *Volcanic Rocks*

Carboniferous Rocks

Barren Red Measures (no coals)
Upper Group of Coals:
Productive Coal Measures
Millstone Grit (no coals)
a *Upper Limestone Group (few coals)*
Lower Group of Coals:
Limestone Coal Group
b *Lower Limestone Group (few or no coals)*
Older Carboniferous Rocks

FIGURE 7. Diagrammatic Horizontal Section across portions of the Scottish coalfields, to show how the rocks have been folded and faulted.

31

the degree of folding and faulting of the rocks. Such a picture is essential in deciding how the coals can be most economically worked.

So far mining has been intensively carried on in the upper series of coals (Productive Coal Measures) and in the lower series (Limestone Coal Group) where the latter are brought up by folding near, or comparatively near, the surface. To-day, accordingly, we find that the large reserves remaining are mainly present in the coals of the Limestone Coal Group, where these lie at depth.

Number of Coal Seams.—One of the difficulties that arise in the development of the Scottish Coalfields is that the number of workable seams in both the upper and lower series of coals varies not only from coalfield to coalfield but even within any particular field. This variation, and the presence of numerous dislocations or faults which interrupt the continuity of the coals, has meant the putting down of many exploratory borings to prove the depth, thickness and quality of the different seams. Borings bring up in sections a solid core of all the rocks cut and these are laid out for examination at the surface. Between 1st January 1948 and 1st January 1958, borings in Scotland amounted to a combined total of approximately seventy-eight miles.

The following table shows the number of workable seams present in some of the principal fields:—

	UPPER SERIES (*Productive Coal Measures*)	LOWER SERIES (*Limestone Coal Group*)
Fife	up to 17	11—16
Central Coalfield (Mainly Lanarkshire)	up to 15	5—11
Midlothian	up to 12	up to 15
East Lothian	—	7—9
North Ayrshire	up to 11	4
Central Ayrshire	6 to 15	3
South Ayrshire (Dailly)	—	5—6
Muirkirk	—	5
Sanquhar	5 or 6	—

In East Lothian, at Muirkirk and at Dailly only the lower series of coals are present, at Sanquhar only the upper seams.

Reserves.—The reserves of coal available in Scotland, in seams of 2 feet or more and at depths up to 4,000 feet, were estimated in 1944 at about 3,300 million tons. Most of the reserves are contained in the lower series of coals in Fife, Clackmannan and Midlothian. In Ayrshire, however, the great bulk of the reserves lie in the Productive Coal Measures. As already stated, mining has so far been largely concentrated in the marginal, shallower portions of the main coalfields and accordingly most of the reserves still to be won lie at depth. That is why it has been essential for the National Coal Board to envisage and plan a considerable number of new collieries, some of which will reach depths of 3,000 feet or slightly more, and to reconstruct and modernise a large number of existing pits.

CHAPTER II

HISTORY OF THE SCOTTISH COAL-MINING INDUSTRY FROM 1100 TO 1700

THE FOLLOWING PARAGRAPHS provide merely an outline of the history and development of the Scottish coal-mining industry in its earlier stages and make no attempt to be comprehensive. For convenience in following the thread of the narrative it has been thought best to set out such notes as are given under period headings, but it must be understood that these necessarily overlap to some extent. The headings are:—(1) The Earliest Records; (2) Period 1300 to 1450; (3) Period 1450 to 1550; and (4) Period 1550 to 1700. The second half of the eighteenth century witnessed the beginnings of the Industrial Revolution, and the main advances in mining practice since then are described in a later chapter.

1. THE EARLIEST RECORDS

We do not know under what circumstances coal was first discovered and used in Scotland. Whether some prehistoric inhabitants, sitting round a brushwood fire, noticed that it had ignited pieces of an outcropping seam, or whether the knowledge of coal was brought into the country by people who had already made use of it, no one can tell. Although coal (*carbones*) is mentioned in documents of the reign of Malcolm IV (1153-65) the first references to systematic working appear in monastic charters of the end of the twelfth century and beginning of the thirteenth. About 1200, for example, the monks of Holyrood Abbey were granted by William de Vipont a tithe of his coal from Carriden; and a few years later (probably between 1210 and 1219) Seyer de Quinci, Earl of Winchester, granted to Newbattle Abbey[1] a coal-works and quarry (*carbonarium et quarrarium*) lying between the burn of Whytrig (or Wygtrig) and the boundaries of Pinkie and Inveresk (not far from Tranent). Some time later (1291) we find that the

---

[1] Newbattle Abbey was founded in 1140 for Cistercian monks from Melrose, the name meaning new building or dwelling. The monks worked coal wherever it outcropped along the banks of the River Esk, as well as on the coast near Prestongrange.

34

monks of Dunfermline Abbey[1] were given the right to work coal on the lands of Pittencrieff, " wherever they wished " but only for their own use and not for sale. About the same time (1294) James, High Steward of Scotland, gave to Paisley Abbey the right of digging sea-coal (*carbones marinos fodiendi*). Such records show that even in these early days coal must have been to some small extent an article of merchandise, but it must be remembered that they do not tell us when coal was actually first worked. Thus, a charter of 1415, belonging to Crossraguel Abbey, Kirkoswald, in Ayrshire, mentions the existence of coal-heughs at Dailly, although here, again, we know nothing of the earlier history of the workings.

These charters, it is true, show that monastic records have often survived while those of the nobility and great land-owners have more often perished. But it is also true that the richly-endowed abbeys and monasteries, during the troubled twelfth, thirteenth and fourteenth centuries, in addition to keeping alive the flame of art and learning, did much to preserve and encourage such local industries as existed in the country around them. Some engaged in the working of coal-heughs and salt-pans[2]; some, again, reared large flocks of sheep and exported wool and wool-fells (that is, skins with the fleece still attached) to the cloth-making towns of the Low Countries. Under their auspices, too, the rough tracks which were the only means of communication between one place and another were improved, bridges were built, and the standard of agriculture raised.

2. PERIOD 1300 TO 1450

During this period coal continued to be produced wherever it could easily be won, although the quantities obtained must have been, by modern standards, very small. Nevertheless the demand for it was slowly increasing and in this the great monastic houses still played an important part. For a long time, however, there was a popular prejudice against the use of coal for domestic

---

[1] Dunfermline Abbey, where the first monks to come to Scotland were installed, was founded in 1075. It also possessed property at Musselburgh.

[2] This was an important industry in coastal areas. Prestonpans, for example, takes its name from the fact that the monks of Newbattle Abbey manufactured salt here by evaporating sea-water in "pans". Other similar place-names are Grangepans, Kennetpans.

purposes, founded on the belief that its smoke and fumes were serious dangers to health.[1]

The English records of the War of Independence and of the occupation of southern Scotland by Edward I and Edward II frequently refer to purchases of coal—usually in association with purchases of iron for the use of a smith. Generally, only the indefinite word " load " is mentioned, but in one entry we find a reference to " eight seams of coal at Linlithgow for Henry the smith", and here a seam meant the load borne by a packhorse. We read also that during the reign of James I and probably in the year 1435, Aeneas Sylvius (later Pope Pius II), while on a visit to Scotland, was amazed to see " the poor, who almost in a state of nakedness begged at the church doors, depart with joy in their faces on receiving stones as alms". And in another account he says: " A sulphurous stone dug from the earth is used by the people as fuel". This was in the Lothians, so that there, at least, coal was already coming into general use.

That the output from the early coal-workings must have been small is clear from the primitive methods that were used. Mining naturally began in places where a coal-seam appeared at the surface, whether along the base of a piece of rising ground, on the sides of a glen, or on the coast. The coal was then won by the simple process of quarrying or digging it out along the actual line of outcrop. The diagram forming Figure 8, for example, shows a coal outcropping on the sides of a glen. At points A1 and A2 small quantities of coal were won by digging or quarrying, and the same process was then repeated at different points along the sides of the glen. When all the coal that could be conveniently reached by this method had been extracted, the miners began to follow the seam underground by driving mines or roads into it. Soon, however, difficulties of drainage and roof-support would become too formidable and the workings would then be abandoned and another mine driven in farther along the outcrop. Again, at point A1 any accumulation of water in the mine would prevent further extraction, but at point A2, where the inclination of the seam provided a natural drainage outlet, the workings could be carried farther underground. Such mines, driven from the surface in the coal itself, became later known as ingaun e'es (ingoing eyes).

[1] It was for this reason that in 1306 an Act was passed forbidding the use of coal in London.

This system was, of course, impracticable where the seam was more or less flat, but still lay at a shallow depth. In these cases the method in use was to sink a short vertical shaft to the coal. The shaft bottom was then widened or " belled out " and as much coal extracted as could be done with safety, the coal being hewn out of the solid and hand-shovelled into baskets (Fig. 9). When abandoned the hole was filled up with the debris from another pit opened up nearby. Even to-day in parts of the coalfields the collapsed shallow workings of these small-scale "bell-pits" still mark the outcrops of some of the thicker seams.

Such primitive mining methods may be described as the *First Stage* in the evolution of the industry. The *Second Stage* was reached with the development of what is sometimes termed the Pit-and-Adit method. This method, illustrated diagrammatically in Figure 10 consisted in driving drainage tunnels (adits or day-levels, as they came to be called) with an outlet at a *lower level* than the workings themselves. In this way any accumulation of water in the mines could escape naturally by gravitation (*e.g.*, at point B in Figure 10). The drainage channels also assisted in minimising ventilation problems.

At this period, fourteenth and early fifteenth centuries, the depths attained by pits was probably not more than 70 or 80 feet. The coal was carried in baskets to the foot of the shaft by adults and children of both sexes known as "bearers" (Fig. 11). In some cases the shafts were provided with ladders, and the bearers had to carry their loads up these " stair-pits " (Fig. 12) to the surface; in others the coal was raised by means of a simple windlass.

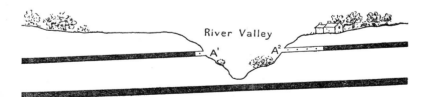

River Valley

A¹   A²

FIGURE 8. Diagram to illustrate early method of working coal at the outcrop. Here the coal is exposed on the sides of a river-gorge. Coal worked is shown by stippling; coal left unworked shown black.

37

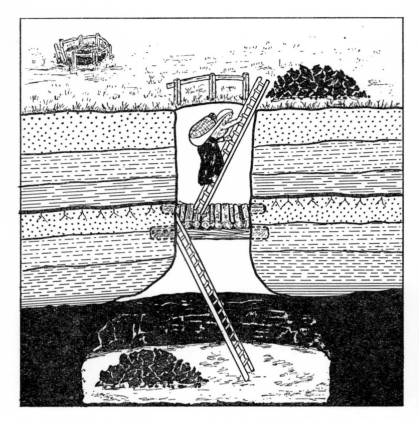

FIGURE 9.   Diagrammatic representation of a Bell-Pit; see text, p. 37.

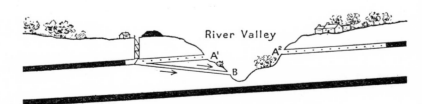

FIGURE 10.   Diagram to illustrate early method of working shallow coals by the Pit-and-Adit System. Ornamentation as in Figure 8; drainage tunnel or day-level shown by arrows.

38

3. PERIOD 1450 to 1550

Few records are available for this period, but it is clear that the demand for coal was expanding in spite of the difficulties attendant on the movement of heavy loads over the rough tracks which at that time and for long afterwards served as roads. On the other hand, many of the coal-heughs bordering the Firth of Forth were able to get comparatively large cargoes away by sea.[1] Demand was also stimulated by the growing scarcity of timber, despite Acts of Parliament ordering the holders of land to plant and preserve trees, and imposing severe penalties upon the destroyers of "green wood".[2] Moreover, coal was being used more and more for industrial purposes.[3]

Increasing demand naturally stimulated the search for sites where coal lay at shallow depths and could be easily won:—in Mid and East Lothian,[4] in West Lothian,[5] in Fife, in Clackmannan, in Ayrshire and elsewhere. That the search was even more widespread is shown by the fact that James IV ordered a survey to be made in Kintyre for coal to supply the royal residences at Tarbert (Loch Fyne) and Dunaverty (Southend)—in the language of the time payment was made to "ane cole man to pas in Kyntyr to vesy gif colis may be wonnyne thare".[6]

At the opening of the sixteenth century the annual output of coal in Scotland probably did not exceed 40,000 tons; and as this output came from places as far apart as East Fife and South Ayrshire it is doubtful if there were as yet many whole-time collieries. Coal-workings were everywhere on a small scale and operated mainly to

---

[1] The monks of Newbattle Abbey constructed a road between Newbattle and the coast near Prestongrange by which coal was taken away for shipment in small boats and salt from the salt pans brought back. This road is still known as the Salters' Road.

[2] Nevertheless, it is said that by the middle of the seventeenth century the Lowlands of Scotland were almost destitute of trees.

[3] It is interesting to note that Hector Boece, a Scottish historian, whose History was published in 1527, says: "In Fyffe ar won black stanis quilk ha sa intollerable heit quhair they are kendillit that they resolve and meltis irne, and are therefore richt proffitable for operation of smithis".

[4] There were coal-heughs belonging to the Crown at Wallyford and Preston in 1542.

[5] We learn that in the reign of James III (1460-88) coal was worked at Bonnytoun, near Bo'ness, for use in Linlithgow Palace.

[6] It may also be noted that coal was discovered at Brora on the East Sutherland coast some time prior to 1569 and worked to some extent for domestic use and salt-making. For Brora coal *see* p. 30.

FIGURE 11. Bearer: it was a common practice in the early days of the industry for the coal to be carried by women, known as bearers, from the working-face to the foot of the shaft. It was not until 1842 that the employment of women and children underground was forbidden by law.

supply local needs. It must be remembered that the population of Scotland in the reign of James IV did not greatly exceed half a million. It must also be remembered that mining methods and appliances were still in their infancy; that pits were limited to a depth of some 90 feet or so, and that any workings were carried out mainly on the Pit-and-Adit system to which reference has already been made. One record of the period (1531) relates to an agreement entered into between the Abbots of Dunfermline and Newbattle defining the manner of working the coal on the margins of their respective lands in the Inveresk-Prestongrange district and providing for the draining away of the mine-water to the sea. Where drainage levels were not possible or practical, water (and coal) was raised in the shafts to the surface by means of a windlass, operated sometimes by horse-labour (horse-gins or horse-engines).

4. PERIOD 1550 to 1700

The next century and a half, which covers the period in Scottish history between the return of the youthful Queen Mary from France (1561) and the Treaty of Union (1707), witnessed an expansion in production that was little short of revolutionary. It has been

FIGURE 12. Diagrammatic representation of a Stair-Pit: women were often employed not only to take the coal from the working-face to the foot of the shaft but also to carry their loads up ladders to the surface. A "load" might amount to $1\frac{1}{2}$ hundredweights.

41

estimated that during that period the annual output increased at least twelvefold from around 40,000 tons to about 500,000 tons. Pit depths, however, were still limited, so that the life of any one sinking was short. It was, accordingly, the custom, when all the coal that could conveniently be reached had been extracted to abandon the pit and to sink a new one a short distance away. New fields were continually being opened up and wrought in this way.

Drainage, however, still remained a formidable obstacle, and it is not until the end of the sixteenth century that we hear, for the first time, of the use of simple machinery to raise the water in mines directly to the surface. This was accomplished by means of what was known as a water-gin (Fig. 13); here a series of wooden buckets were attached to an endless chain passing over an axle stretched across the pit-mouth, the axle being operated by a large wheel turned by water power. Such water-wheels were also used for raising coal in baskets. Sometimes a similar mechanism was operated by horse-labour (Fig. 14) and occasionally, in exposed situations, by windmills. With their advent the industry may be said to have reached the *Third* or *Pit Stage* of development.

. To illustrate the quickening tempo of the industry, reference may be made to the outstanding advances made by Sir George Bruce of Carnock, who, between 1590 and 1625, established an important coal-mining and salt-making industry a little west of Culross. This colliery had two shafts, one on the land close to the shore from which the workings extended for about half a mile under the foreshore to a second shaft sunk below high-water mark. This shaft was protected by a raised mound against flooding so that, except at low tides, it was actually an island. This was the celebrated Moat Pit, as it was termed, and its purpose was to allow of coal being more easily shipped.

The growing interest then being taken in mechanical drainage methods is shown by a statement, made in 1598, that Gavin Smith, the Englishman, and James Aitchison, King James IV's goldsmith, had invented an " artificial engine " or " pomp", for raising water out of mines and coal-heughs and to be worked by wind, water, horse or men, whereby flooded workings could be brought into use again.

Bruce's Moat Pit also demonstrated the advantage of having two shafts and so permitting a free circulation of air underground. As the provision of two separate means of egress from a mine was

FIGURE 13. Water-Gin: a machine formerly used for raising coal in shallow shafts; the wheel was operated by water. (From *A Glossary of Scotch Mining Terms*, by J. Barrowman, 1886.)

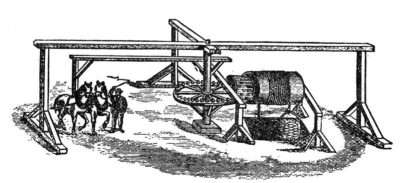

FIGURE 14. Horse-Gin: a machine formerly used for raising coal in shallow shafts; it was operated by horse-labour, hence the terms horse-gin or horse-engine. (From *A Glossary of Scotch Mining Terms*, by J. Barrowman, 1886.)

not made compulsory for over 250 years (in 1852 to be precise), we can see how far Bruce was in advance of his time. Fans, however, had not yet been discovered and in almost all mines fires continued to be lighted in order to set up a draught and keep fresh air circulating through the workings.

With the arrival of the seventeenth century we get a clearer picture of what was happening. The shores of the Firth of Forth were becoming studded with coal-pits. As the century progressed the number of mines in Fife rose until there were more than fifty pits of considerable size, some producing as much as 15,000 tons a year. Indeed, in spite of the troubled state of Scotland there was a remarkable expansion in mining activity, due primarily to the increasing demands for coal made by the manufacturing industries, particularly in the second half of the century. Ever-increasing quantities of coal were wanted for the brewing, pottery, glass, soap and other trades, as well as for salt production and the burning of limestone in kilns.

It is not until towards the close of the century, however, that we begin to hear more about the mining industry in the West of Scotland, particularly around Glasgow and in North Ayrshire. An important development in the latter district was set on foot in 1690 by Sir George Cunningham, who sank the " deep shank " pit at Stevenston, an undertaking notable for the fact that a bore was first put down to prove the coals. About 1700 he constructed a harbour at Saltcoats, said to have been " large and enterprising". This was Ayrshire's first large-scale mining venture and it was Cunningham's intention to export coal " wherewith that country abounds " and salt, especially to the expanding Irish market.[1]

By 1690, we read, water-wheels (or water-gins) were in common use in Scotland, but these and other similar methods of raising water and coal from the pits were costly to maintain, while the depth to which they could operate was limited. By the end of the century, too, much of the coal in the coastal areas that lay above sea-level (that is, the coal in workings that could be drained by day-levels to the shore) was nearing exhaustion.

The coming of the eighteenth century, however, brought a new development to the assistance of the industry—the " raising of water by fire". This was the famous atmospheric steam-engine of

---

[1] The name Saltcoats means the salters' cots or huts.

Thomas Newcomen, an English inventor who was born at Dartmouth in 1663. Newcomen's invention was patented in 1705 and by 1712 had been adapted for use in collieries. The first of these engines to be erected in Scotland for the purpose of overcoming one of mining's greatest hazards, the heavy accumulation of water in workings, was at Elphinstone Colliery, near Airth, in Stirlingshire, about 1720. This was followed by the erection of a similar one in 1725 at Edmonstone Colliery, Midlothian. These steam-engines were little understood at the time, besides being costly to erect, operate and maintain, so that it is not surprising to find from contemporary accounts that many mines were worked only while the coal could be won "dry" and were then abandoned without any attempt to instal the new "fire-engine".

None the less, as we shall learn in the next chapter, the " fire-engine " had come to stay.

CHAPTER III

HISTORY OF THE SCOTTISH COAL-MINING INDUSTRY FROM 1700 TO 1850

The story of the coal-mining industry from the twelfth century to the end of the seventeenth has been outlined in the previous chapter. It now remains to trace its development during the crowded years that followed. Here again the main events are dealt with under period headings.

PERIOD 1700 to 1750

The first half of the eighteenth century was, for Scotland, a time of depression and frustration. At the beginning of the period it was not nearly so prosperous a country as England and, indeed, lagged far behind the latter as regards industrial development, agricultural practice and foreign trade. It is true that the Treaty of Union (1707) opened the markets of the New World to Scottish traders, hitherto restricted mainly to commerce with the Low Countries and Scandinavia. But there was a long leeway to make up and a good many years had to elapse before Scotland really benefited from the removal of the barriers that had hitherto prevented her from sharing in the lucrative trade enjoyed by England with her overseas Colonies. In 1707, for example, the merchant fleet of Glasgow (then with a population of some 12,500) numbered only fifteen small vessels which had to unload their cargoes at Port Glasgow and transfer them to boats for conveyance to the city twenty miles or so higher up the Clyde. Agricultural methods, too, were still primitive and, indeed, in the country districts a bad harvest often resulted in conditions bordering on famine. The state of such roads or rough tracks that existed hindered the free interchange of goods between districts that could not be served by sea or river transport. The Jacobite uprisings of 1715 and 1745 must also have had an adverse effect on the peaceful pursuit of trade and industry.

The economic depression had its repercussions in the coal-mining industry. By the middle of the century collieries had in many cases reached depths[1] at which none of the drainage methods

---

[1] Up to about 240 feet.

known could cope with the incoming mine-waters. Even where the Newcomen "fire-engine" (p. 45) could be installed, its range was limited,[1] while its initial cost and the need for skilled labour to operate and maintain it put it out of reach of any but the larger coal-mining concerns. As underground workings extended, the problem of drainage became more and more acute, while there was, in addition, an increasing risk of explosions from accumulations of "fire-damp" (methane gas) at the working faces. Various attempts were made to improve ventilation and keep a current of air moving through the underground roads, but none of these proved satisfactory. The two vital difficulties of drainage and ventilation appeared insuperable, and in many cases workings had to be abandoned and collieries shut down. It seemed, indeed, as if an impasse had been reached and that no further progress was possible. A new incentive was required to dispel the feeling of frustration and fortunately this incentive was soon to be forthcoming in the steam-engine of James Watt.

PERIOD 1750 to 1800

The second half of the eighteenth century witnessed a vast transformation of the whole Scottish scene. It was a period of rapid and unprecedented progress in the economic and social life of the country. It seemed, indeed, as if the long pent-up energy of the Scottish people had been suddenly released. New industries multiplied, new agricultural methods were introduced, and the demand for goods for both home and foreign markets expanded vigorously.

It was during these years that we find the beginnings of what is known as the Industrial Revolution, a revolution which ushered in the age of steam-power and mechanisation. By far the most important event in this period was the coming of the improved steam-engine of James Watt (1736–1819). It was while he was engaged on the repair of a model of the Newcomen engine at Glasgow University in 1763 that he was struck with the wastage of steam involved in the alternate heating and cooling of the cylinder in which the piston

---

[1] In the Newcomen engine the steam admitted to the cylinder during the upward stroke of the piston had to be condensed by the injection of jets of cold water; the downward stroke of the piston was effected by atmospheric pressure. Hence the term " atmospheric " often used to describe this early type of steam-engine.

worked. To remedy this defect he had the brilliant inspiration of using a separate condenser, that is, a vessel into which the steam could escape and be condensed independently of the cylinder. The first of the new engines was erected in 1768 at the Burn Pit, Kinneil. Improvement after improvement followed and by 1784 Watt had perfected his double-acting rotative steam-engine; double acting because both ends of the cylinder were connected alternately to the condenser and steam-power used for both strokes of the piston; rotative because it was designed to give a continuous revolving motion to a shaft provided with a flywheel. The steam-engine could now be employed to drive machinery of all kinds and the age of steam-power had arrived.

To the mining industry the steam-engine brought fresh hopes and the promise of a new life. The gloom and the sense of frustration which had hung over it for many years were dispelled. It had now at hand a powerful instrument with which to tackle the problems of draining waterlogged workings and of raising both coal and water from increasing depths. This implied, of course, that many seams hitherto out of reach could now be wrought. A contemporary of Watt, writing in 1812,[1] speaks of the new engine as "the most complete and powerful of any that the philosophy and genius of man have presented to the world". From the same authority we learn that while "it was only in the beginning of the eighteenth century that pits of 80 yards deep were to be found in Scotland", yet by the beginning of the nineteenth century "we now find in Scotland pits of 140 yards, and in England no less than 300 yards deep".

A second major event was the rise of the iron industry, which was to attain a remarkable expansion in the nineteenth century. Hitherto iron had been made in Scotland on a small scale in districts where wood-charcoal could be easily got. The ore was smelted in small primitive furnaces, known as bloomeries, worked either by natural draught or by an artificial blast produced by means of bellows. The crude iron (pig-iron) obtained in this way was freed from adhering slag and was then reheated and hammered out or moulded by smiths into a variety of articles—tools, implements, weapons, ornamental iron-work, etc. By the middle of the eighteenth century, however, improvements in blast-furnace construction had opened the way for the use of coal-coke in the smelting of iron, and with the

[1] Robert Bald, Civil Engineer and Mineral Surveyor, "A general View of the Coal Trade of Scotland . . .". Edinburgh, 1812.

erection of the first furnace at Carron in 1760 the centuries-old practice of employing wood-charcoal was nearing an end.[1] Fortunately for the industry, also, ample supplies of raw materials were available in the clayband ironstones[2] found in association with the coals in the Carboniferous rocks. It was at Carron that this type of ore was first used; initially it was smelted by wood-charcoal but with the transition to coal-coke[3] about 1770 the foundations of the great Scottish iron industry were laid.

Other factors which contributed to the growing national prosperity and hence led, directly or indirectly, to a vastly increased demand for coal were:—

(a) The improvement in means of transport and communications following upon the introduction, about 1750, of the turnpike[4] system and the setting up of turnpike trusts empowered to construct and maintain the roads in the more populated districts; the completion of the Forth and Clyde Canal in 1790, followed by other canals, such as the Monkland Canal; and the opening up of the Highlands after the Jacobite uprisings.[5] It must not be assumed, however, that the roads of this period were roads in the modern sense. They were still very imperfect[6] and often in bad weather difficult and even dangerous for wheeled traffic. Indeed, it was not until the early part of the nineteenth century that road-making was revolutionised by the work of Macadam and Telford (see p. 52).

---

[1] With the continued scarcity of timber (see p. 39) the making of iron came to be confined latterly to the wooded glens of the western Highlands, where wood-charcoal was used to smelt haematite ore imported from Cumberland. Thus, at different periods during the eighteenth century the following furnaces were in operation: Invergarry; Lorne Furnace, Bonawe; and Goatfield Furnace on Loch Fyne, eight miles south of Inveraray. The last two continued working into the nineteenth century.

[2] Iron in the form of iron carbonate ($Fe CO_3$), occurring frequently as beds, or layers of closely-packed nodules, in the shales overlying coals. The iron-ore is mixed with a variable amount of clay material and hence comes the name clayband ironstone.

[3] That is, coal converted to coke by heating it so as to drive off the volatile matter and leave a residue rich in carbon. Originally it was made in the open by building up blocks of coal into circular heaps with a central cavity and apertures for air, and then setting them on fire. When the mass had swollen up and become spongy it was covered up with ashes to exclude air and prevent further combustion.

[4] A barrier, generally a horizontal beam of timber moving on a vertical pillar, designed to stop traffic until the toll had been paid.

[5] The construction of the military roads through the Highlands, carried out by General Wade's army between 1726 and 1740, was the first step.

[6] The journey by stage-coach from Edinburgh to London in 1763 took fourteen days.

(b) The deepening of the River Clyde, which began about 1773 and continued until sea-going vessels were able to sail directly to and from Glasgow; the rapid growth of that city as a commercial centre,[1] and the beginnings of the industrialisation of Clydeside.

(c) The expanding trade during the middle decades of the eighteenth century with the American and West Indian Colonies, by which tobacco and sugar (mainly) were imported in exchange for goods manufactured at home, e.g. coarse cloth, linen, pottery, glassware, soap, leather, etc. This trade came to an end with the outbreak of the American War of Independence (1775-83), and was replaced from 1785 by the raw cotton boom. By 1800 the manufacture of cotton goods of all kinds, centred largely around Glasgow and Paisley, was Scotland's most thriving industry.[2]

(d) The striking progress made in agricultural practices, including the use of iron in place of wood for farm implements, the introduction of a wider range of crops and of a system of crop rotation, and the increasing use of lime as a fertiliser.

The combined effect of all these advances in the industrial and social life of Scotland was to create rapidly expanding markets for coal, an expansion that continued with an increasing impetus into the nineteenth century.

PERIOD 1800 to 1850

This period may perhaps be best described as the Coal and Iron Age. It was an age, also, which saw steam power harnessed to a variety of purposes and manufactures. Robert Bald (see footnote p. 48), writing in 1812, gives as the main reasons for the increased consumption of coal in Scotland:—

" 1st, The style of living is altered in a great degree, compared with what it was fifty years ago, so that a person of the same class of society keeps at least double, if not treble, the number of fires in his house, and this alteration is very conspicuous in our cities.

" 2nd, The extension of the iron trade—the rapid distillation of spirits—the manufacture of glass—the numerous steam-engines employed in all kinds of work, besides a very great number of

---

[1] The population of Glasgow rose from 12,500 in 1707 to 83,000 in 1801 and to 202,000 by 1831.

[2] The cotton mills were at first run by water-power and among the earliest to be set up were those at New Lanark.

manufactories on a less scale, such as potteries, tile-works, breweries, soap-works, etc.

" 3rd, The burning of lime [limestone], particularly for the purposes of agriculture.

" This last trade may be said to be only in its infancy. The consumption of coal for this purpose within the last fifteen years is truly surprising."

It will be seen that in the passage quoted Bald speaks of the " very conspicuous " increase in the demand for coal in the cities. It was in the last years of the eighteenth century and the early part of the nineteenth that the process of urbanisation began, that is, the change from the condition of a population scattered mainly in small communities, villages and burghs to one of towns, factories and machines. Larger and larger supplies of coal were needed for the new industrial centres and the story of coal-mining throughout this period is one of continued endeavour to meet ever-growing demands. A widespread search for new fields of coal and ironstone took place. There already existed a very considerable body of information about the broad distribution and limits of the coal-field areas, though little had so far been done to prove any but the very shallow seams. With steam power now available to raise the coal from ever-increasing depths and to deal with the age-long problem of drainage, the way was open for an intensive programme of exploration of the deeper basins of coal. Many hundreds of trial borings for coal and ironstone were put down and on the results of these, new collieries were sited and sunk. Boring was carried out by percussion drilling, that is, by driving down a boring chisel or auger to the necessary depth and obtaining small pieces of the different types of rocks passed through. This was a slow, laborious operation and it was not until well on in the century that depths of 1,000 feet or so were possible.[1] Shaft depths were also gradually increased and workings extended to greater and greater distances from the shafts themselves. New techniques were developed to deal with the extended scales of operations; improvements in methods of pit construction and winding equipment such as the provision of winding cages and guide-ropes; improvements in underground haulage methods to convey the coal from the

[1] Boring by rotary diamond drill, by which a solid core of the rocks passed through is obtained and brought to the surface for detailed examination, did not come into use until about 1870.

working faces to the bottom of the shafts; improvements in underground ventilation, culminating with the gradual introduction of the fan-system during the latter part of the nineteenth century.

Meanwhile new discoveries and inventions were being made, new industries were springing up and new methods of transport were being developed, all of them, in one way or another, creating heavy and increasing demands for coal and ironstone. It will not be out of place to refer briefly to some of the main advances which the Industrial Revolution brought in its train and in many of which Scottish engineers and scientists played an important part. In this connection it must not be forgotten that it was the improved steam-engine of Watt which initiated the era of rapid industrial development during the early decades of the nineteenth century. Associated with Watt in his work at Birmingham was another Scotsman, William Murdoch (1754-1839), born at Bellow Mill, Lugar, and whose experiments to use coal-gas as a general illuminant came to fruition in 1812. In the early days of the gas industry the coal was distilled or " carbonised " in iron retorts, the products being gas, tar and a coke residue. Gas of course was regarded as the essential product of the process,[1] with coke as a by-product, but the tar was then looked upon largely as a nuisance. Some of it, however, found a use as a preservative coating for timber and iron-work. About 1815 it was discovered that coal-tar itself could be distilled, giving as crude products creosotes, oils and pitch, and one of the crude oils of coal-tar distillation was used by Charles Macintosh (1766-1843) in Glasgow in the making of waterproof material. It was not until the second half of the nineteenth century, however, that we find the beginnings of the now vast industry based on coal-tar distillation derivatives.

In the early years of the century, also, came the great advance in road-construction methods inspired by the two famous engineers John Loudon Macadam (1756-1836) and Thomas Telford (1757-1834). Macadam, who was born in Ayr, began his experiments in road-improvement in Ayrshire and continued them in the south of England. His methods of surfacing roads by laying down a 10-inch thick bed of " broken stone which shall unite by its own angles to

---

[1] Since it was the illuminating power of the gas that was the important factor, cannel coal, a type rich in volatile matter, was in great demand for gas-making. Later, with the incoming of the incandescent mantle, the actual heating properties of the gas were more important and the use of cannel (or candle) coal became unnecessary.

PLATE 3

Copy of an old engraving showing the great steam pumping-engine built by Claud Girdwood & Co., Glasgow, and erected at Newcraighall Colliery, Edinburgh in 1828. The enormous cast-iron beam, receiving its motion from the 80-inch diameter piston of a double-acting steam cylinder, raised and lowered the shaft pump-rods through an 8-foot stroke thirteen times every minute. These rods, hanging in the shaft, operated pumps lifting the drainage water to the surface in several stages. Nothing now remains of the pumping-engine, but from the engraving it would appear to have been the largest of its type in Scotland.

PLATE 4—Remains of a Newcomen atmospheric steam engine.

PLATE 5—Beam engine made by Walkinshaw, Glasgow about 1790.

form a hard solid surface "[1] was widely adopted as cheaper than that put forward by Telford. The latter, who came from Eskdale in Dumfriesshire, was a well-known civil engineer of the time, employed on canal, harbour, bridge and road construction works.[2] A result of the improvement in the main roads was the speeding up of wheeled traffic and the speed of stage-coaches rose from five to as much as twelve miles per hour.[3] Actually the years between 1820 and 1836 were the "golden days" of the stage-coach but with the coming of the railways it rapidly disappeared from the scene.

The Railway Age may be said to date from 1825 when the first passenger train, drawn by a Stephenson locomotive, ran between Stockport and Darlington. It may be noted that Stephenson (1781-1848) in his early days was fireman of a colliery engine near Newcastle and that his first "travelling engine" (so-called to distinguish it from a stationary engine) was built in 1814 to transport coal from Killingworth Colliery to Newcastle, a distance of nine miles. The application of the steam-engine to railways was a major revolution in methods of transport and enormously accelerated the rate of industrial expansion. It meant, for example, that the days of the old tramways or wagonways, with wooden rails and small wagons drawn by horses, which for over a century had served to take coal from the mines to industrial centres or to the sea-ports for shipment, were gone for ever.[4] Later, the advent of the great era of railway construction[5] between 1836 and 1856, led to not only a vastly increased outlet for coal to meet the expanding home and export markets but also a demand for iron for structural purposes of all kinds. It also made possible a much more rapid distribution of raw materials and of the products of industry and agriculture.

The output of coal in Scotland is estimated to have increased

---

[1] The use of asphalt or pitch as a binding medium did not come into use until 1867.

[2] Telford was engineer for the Caledonian Canal, for the Dean Bridge, Edinburgh and for the Broomielaw Bridge, Glasgow.

[3] Stage-coaches had been in use in Britain for a long time but seldom covered more than between forty and fifty miles in a day of twelve hours.

[4] A number of these old wagonways were in operation in Scotland during the eighteenth century, one of the earliest (if not the earliest) taking coal from the Tranent area to the coast at Cockenzie. Many of them, relaid with iron rails, continued well on into the nineteenth century.

[5] In particular, the construction of railways in Lanarkshire gave enormous impetus to the opening up of the coal and ironstone fields in the West. Hitherto, the Monkland Canal had served as the main link between Coatbridge and Glasgow.

from about 475,000 tons towards the end of the seventeenth century to about 1,600,000 tons towards the end of the eighteenth. During the first half of the nineteenth century it rose rapidly, reaching about 17,000,000 tons by 1873. A parallel advance is shown by the output of pig iron and of iron ore. The output of pig iron has been estimated to have increased from nearly 23,000 tons in 1806 to 37,500 tons in 1830. Between 1830 and 1835 output was doubled, this sudden rise following the use of the blackband ironstones of the Carboniferous rocks. Blackband ironstone differs from the clayband ores (*see* footnote 2, p. 49) in that it contains in itself sufficient coal to make it self-calcining. Actually the first blackband was discovered in 1801 and though it was recognised as a potential ore it was not until 1828 that it was found possible to use this type of ore in the blast-furnaces of the time. This great advance was due to the introduction of the hot blast by Neilson, that is, by the use of pre-heated air, under pressure, in place of the cold air blast hitherto employed. A great increase in the number of furnaces followed, and the output of pig iron rose to some 197,000 tons in 1840, to 475,000 tons in 1845 and to 775,000 tons by 1852. The sudden increase after 1845 was due largely to the demands made for railway extensions and other constructional work, and for a steadily expanding industry in heavy engineering.

CHAPTER IV

CONDITIONS OF LIFE AND WORK IN EARLY SCOTTISH COAL MINES

HAVING TRACED the gradual growth of coal mining in Scotland from about the beginning of the thirteenth century, let us see what we know of the social surroundings and physical conditions under which the men, women and children toiled to win the coal. In reading this account of life and work in the mines, it must always be remembered that the living standards of all classes of the community were immeasurably lower than to-day.

From the thirteenth century, when the records of coal mining in Scotland first emerge, until the end of the fifteenth century there is little direct information about the working and living conditions of the colliers and their families. Mining was probably a seasonal occupation when those with no better means of livelihood in winter betook themselves to the coal-heughs to win winter fuel for the immediate needs of their employers.

But the demand for coal steadily grew, as may be clearly seen from various Acts passed by Parliament during the sixteenth century. In 1563 and 1579 Acts were passed against the export of coal which led to " exhorbitant derth and scantnes of fewall ". These Acts were renewed in 1585 and 1597; and in 1592 persons maliciously setting coal-heughs on fire were to be punished as guilty of treason.[1]

Confronted by a pressing shortage of coal and determined to prevent miners leaving their work, the Scots Parliament passed an infamous Act in 1606 which reduced not only the colliers but also the salters to a state of abject servitude. At all costs, the collier must be kept to the coal-heughs! His position under the new Act differed from that of the slave only in that his master had not the power to bring him out of the mine and dispose of him by public auction in the market place. The opening up of new collieries had led the new owners, having no trained workmen of their own, to entice experienced workmen from established collieries by means of gifts and promises of higher wages. This was strongly resented by

---

[1] Shortly after the latter Act was passed, one John Henrie, of Little Fawside, was hanged at the Market Cross of Edinburgh for wilfully setting fire to the colliery.

their former masters, and in the Act of 1606 it was ordained that no person should fee, hire or conduce (take away) any salters, colliers or coalbearers without a written authority from the master whom they had last served: otherwise their former masters could reclaim them " within a year and a day " and the colliers or coalbearers who had accepted wages from their new masters were to be regarded as thieves and punished accordingly. And in 1641 the Act of 1606 was extended to enslave other classes of workers in the coal mines—namely, the watermen, windsmen and gatesmen.

Moreover, these now enslaved colliers were to work all six days of the week with no holiday save that of the seventh day. The concluding paragraph of the Act of 1641 states that " because the said coal-hewers and salters and other workmen in coal-heughs within this Kingdom do lie from their work at Pasch, Yule, Whit Sunday and certain other times in the year, which times they employ in drinking and debauchery, to the great offence of God and prejudice of their master, it is therefore Statute and ordained that the said coal-hewers and salters, and other workmen of coal-heughs in this Kingdom, work all the six days of the week under the pains following:—That is to say that every coal-hewer or salter who lies idle shall pay twenty shillings for every day, by and attour the prejudice sustained by their master, and other punishment of their bodies ".[1]

The Act of 1606 had also given powers to the owners of coal-heughs to apprehend vagabonds and sturdy beggars and put them to labour. And when in 1672 an Act was passed for the establishment of workhouses where the poor, vagabonds and idle could be set to work, the powers already granted to coal masters in 1606 were confirmed. They could seize upon any vagabonds or beggars wherever they could find them, and put them to work in the coal-heughs or other manufactories. And the words "other manufactories" are important, for as we have seen Scotland was just beginning to become industrialised.

With Acts such as those of 1606 and 1641, and with the pressing (conscription) of vagabonds and sturdy beggars, colliers and coalbearers were hardly likely to be accepted as the social equals of the rest of the community. Or again, when colliers were at best

---

[1] Though we have records of some pits in the Saltcoats district in the early eighteenth century where the " hewers " and " bearers " were working only a five-day week.

recruited from agricultural labourers who were for one reason or another unable to secure regular employment on the land, or at the worst from among prisoners-of-war and criminals, they entered their occupation more or less condemned in advance to fill a degraded position in the social order. They were paid more than other labourers; the records reveal that they were better off in worldly goods; yet there was a stigma attached to coal mining, and the colliers were regarded as a class apart.

In or about the year 1700 the population of Scotland was approximately 1,000,000. At that time the output of coal was around 500,000 tons per annum, from which it has been estimated that the manpower engaged (all classes) would be about 3,000. The total number of persons dependent on mining would thus be about 15,000, living chiefly near the shores of the Firth of Forth and spreading into Lanarkshire and Ayrshire.

While the early decades of the eighteenth century witnessed changes and developments in the realms of politics, religion, arts and letters it is difficult to detect any commensurate improvement in the economic and social conditions of the poorer classes. Most of the population were engaged in agriculture. In the opening years of the century we know that poverty was rampant and misery widespread. It was estimated by a contemporary writer that one-fifth of the people were living in a state of beggary. As for the colliers, we need only note that when, in 1701, Parliament introduced an important Act to prevent wrongous imprisonment and undue delays in trials (a *Habeas Corpus* Act for Scotland) there appeared in the body of the Statute a clause stating that " this present Act is no wayes to be extended to colliers or salters".

The colliers were " a class apart". The Acts of 1606 and 1641 had been ratified in 1661 and, by interpretation, were now held to mean that, by accepting work in a colliery, the worker became " astricted " (bound) thereto for the rest of his life. If the colliery were sold, he went with it—and his children also, for, if a collier's son or daughter once worked in the mine, that child was henceforth bound to the mine like the father.

Neither the people nor the Government had any particular animosity against the collier—in fact, a great deal of sympathy was felt towards them. And there is some evidence that the " servitude " of colliers, re-affirmed in 1661, was not strictly enforced. But social welfare was not considered a rational let alone a practical

57

proposition in those days. They were miners and that was that. The poor agricultural labourer, too, earned his few odd shillings a week. He, too, had his dues. What more was there to it?

Throughout the eighteenth century, then, men, women and children, might be working underground; many men and women worked there from childhood to the grave. The menfolk howked the coal and the women and children dragged it or carried it to the pit-bottom and then up stairs or ladders to the surface. Slypes (sleds) or hurlies (barrows) were the only alternatives for the back-breaking burdens of these wretched people.

There are no records which tell us when this degrading practice of sending women and children to work underground began; and, strange to say, none of the early historians takes any notice of the practice. It had long been the common custom for the members of the same family to work together on the land as a team, and no doubt in times of agricultural depression many of these poor families moved en bloc to the mines, the salt pans, or to any other kind of work that offered. Moreover, so far as the children were concerned, there was no free schooling. What was there for children to do, save work and help the family income? And similar appalling conditions of female and child labour were to be found in the new factories that were now springing up.

The hours worked underground each day were seldom less than twelve, and often as much as fifteen or sixteen; and that, together with the drab and depressing conditions of the colliers' life and work naturally led to some rude licence and hard drinking. Their homes were generally of a squalid description, and completely lacking those small comforts which only a woman's hand might have supplied had not mothers (and daughters) themselves been engaged in this soul-destroying occupation. The lot of the agricultural labourer, despite his lower earnings compared to the miner's, was probably much happier. He might be ejected from his cottage, his wife and children might have to share with him the task of earning the livelihood, but he could offer his labour yearly at a " feeing fair " and he and his family had a measure of freedom. Above all, they were usually at work in the open air and frequently in receipt of various allowances from the produce of the farm. Often they had a " kail yard", poultry and even a cow of their own.

The Scottish laws binding the colliers to their work were repealed by Acts passed in 1775 and 1799. The Act of 1775 was not dictated solely by humanitarian sentiments but partly by economic necessity, it no longer being found possible to keep the colliers in strict servitude. The preamble to the Act states that " many colliers and salters are in a state of slavery and bondage", and also gives the clue:—" There are not a sufficient number of colliers, coal-bearers, and salters in Scotland for working the quantity of coal necessarily wanted and many new discovered coals remain unwrought; nor are there a sufficient number of salters for salt works, to the great loss of the owners and disadvantage to the public".

The Act stipulated that no person who henceforth began to work as a collier in Scotland was to be bound in any other way than were other servants. Persons under twenty-one years of age employed in the mines were to become free after seven years further service, as also were all bound colliers above thirty-five and under forty-five, but the period was extended to ten years for those between the ages of twenty-one and thirty-five. Bound colliers over forty-five were to be set free after three years. The liberation of the father was declared to liberate his family; and the colliers, when freed, were to enjoy the protection of the Act of 1701. But the colliers might be called upon by their masters to find and instruct apprentices, and if they failed to do so properly their bondage was to last three years longer than the time specified.

The Act of 1775 was effective in checking new slavery, but a radical defect robbed it of its efficiency in respect of those bound colliers engaged in mining at the date when the Act came into force. Instead of becoming free by the mere lapse of time the collier had to make a formal legal application before the sheriff—a deterrent to all save a few. Moreover, many of the colliers did not at first appreciate their new rights. Some, because of their intense desire for security, were quite willing to abandon liberty. The mere fact that the master was obliged to keep his serfs all their days, in sickness and old age, was to some colliers at least adequate compensation for their lot.[1] A great many of the colliers continued in slavery till 1799 when Parliament enacted that all colliers in Scotland who were still bound were, from the passing of the Act to " be free from their servitude".

---

[1] From a manuscript of 1712, quoted in Grossart's *History of Shotts*, the rules for bound colliers in that district included—" weekly allowances to the collier of one or two pecks of meal, when sick; at his marriage the payment of £5.16.0d Scots, ten quarters of iron and deals, or a tree to make a bed ".

More than forty years had still to pass before it became unlawful to employ women and children underground.

APPENDIX

Henry Cockburn, who was a young advocate in 1800 and who was later to become a judge of the Court of Session, wrote feelingly about the colliers and salters in relation to the Acts of 1775 and 1799.[1]

" There are few people who now know that so recently as 1799 there were slaves in this country (Scotland). Twenty-five years before, that is, in 1775, there must have been thousands of them; for this was then the condition of all our colliers and salters. They were literally slaves. They could not be killed nor directly tortured; but they belonged, like the serfs of an older time, to their respective works, with which they were sold as a part of the gearing. With a few very rigid exceptions, the condition of the head of the family was the condition of the whole house. For though a child, *if never entered* with the work, was free, yet entering was its natural and almost certain destination; for its doing so was valuable to its father, and its getting into any other employment in the neighbourhood was resisted by the owner. So that wives, daughters, and sons went on from generation to generation under the system which was the family doom. Of course it was the interest of a wise master to use them well, as it was to use his other cattle well. But, as usual, the human animal had the worst of it. It had rights, and could provoke by alluding to them. It could alarm and mutiny. It could not be slain, but it had no protection against fits of tyranny or anger. We do not now know much of their exact personal or domestic condition. But we know what their work makes them, even when they are free, and within the jealous benevolence of a softer age. We know that they formed a separate and avoided tribe, as to a great extent they still do, with a language and habits of their own. And we know what slavery even in its best form is, and does."

Then, after citing the two Acts of 1775 and 1799 which broke the " chain of slavery", he concludes significantly:—

" These two statutes seem to have been neither the effect nor the cause of any public excitement. I do not see either of them even mentioned in the *Scots Magazine*. People cared nothing about colliers on their own account. . . ."

[1] *Memorials of His Time*, 1910 edn., pp. 70-72.

PLATE 6—WINDING DEVELOPMENTS.   Electric winding engine at a Scottish colliery.

(*See text, page 79*)

PLATE 7—MECHANICAL DECKING.   Two transporters handling mine cars at the tipplers.

PLATE 8—JOY CONTINUOUS MINER. For high productivity in thick coal.

PLATE 9—MODERN UNDERGROUND TRANSPORT. Diesel locomotive drawing train of mine cars.

CHAPTER V

TECHNICAL PROGRESS
DURING THE LAST 100 YEARS

WITHIN THE PAST HUNDRED YEARS the application of power-driven machinery has changed our way of life and raised living standards to a level higher than ever before. As in other industries, the manual effort demanded in coal-mining is much less than it was a century ago, and is steadily being reduced. Some of the principal developments in the use of mechanical power to which reference is made in this Chapter have not only conferred lasting benefit on the coal industry, but have been largely pioneered by the mining engineers and their associates.

By 1850, Scotland was already in the van of the Industrial Revolution, her geographical position, expanding railway system and waterways enabling her industrialists to make full use of the indigenous raw materials, such as coal and ironstone, which were available to them. Clydeside was already becoming one of the greatest centres of heavy industry in the world, specialising in the design and construction of marine and land boilers and engines, in the building of ships and locomotives, and in the manufacture of plant and machinery generally.

The coal industry, too, was making a vigorous effort to introduce new mechanical aids to production. Steam had been, of course, in use for pumping long before 1850 and its application to winding and coal transport was growing year by year, marking a considerable advance on the position at the beginning of the nineteenth century. Coalface operations in 1850, however, were still exclusively manual, and, indeed, even half a century later, the position so far as face-work was concerned showed little change.

There were in those days few text-books and fewer training facilities for engineering students and apprentices to compare with the present, the engineer of a century ago being more or less obliged to rely on his own ingenuity and skill. Technical colleges and professional bodies, or associations,[1] such as we have to-day, were

[1] The first British Mining Institute, properly so-called, was the North of England Institute of Mining and Mechanical Engineers, founded in 1852. The Mining Institute of Scotland dates from 1878. The oldest constituent member of the Institution of Mining Engineers is the old Manchester Geological Society, which changed its name in 1903 to the Manchester Geological and Mining Society. This body federated with the Institution of Mining Engineers in 1904.

unknown, while the mildly sceptical attitude of many of the colliery owners to "these new-fangled ideas and machines" had also to be overcome.

The mining engineer was handicapped also by the lack of suitable metals with which to fashion machines strong and tough enough to withstand the strain and wear-and-tear of mining for, it should be remembered, hard alloy steels had not yet been invented, while the too-brittle and inferior steel that was available was unreliable. As a result, coal production was constantly interrupted by breakdowns when new mechanical devices were being tried out and many tentative projects were either delayed or abandoned completely.

PROVING THE COALS

The first thing the mining engineer has to do is to get to know all he can about the coals which he proposes to work. This he does by drilling boreholes down through the coal-bearing strata to test the exact position, thickness and quality of the seams. The bores will also tell the engineer whether there is any abnormal variation in the geological succession, the direction of faulting and folding, and whether there are any igneous intrusions which may have affected the workability and characteristics of the coals. This information he will use to supplement the general information' he has already obtained from the records of other collieries which have operated in the vicinity.

The earliest method was to drill small-diameter holes into the strata, using rods or ropes to which chisels or drilling bits were attached. By raising and dropping the heavy drill-head, a succession of sharp blows was delivered with a turning movement which enabled the rock to be cut, known as percussion drilling. Around the middle of last century, when the steam engine was brought into use for boring purposes, a new method known as rotary drilling was evolved—a further improvement being the use of hollow rods enabling the bore debris to be water-flushed to the surface for examination.

About the year 1870, the diamond-studded crown was introduced, enabling a complete core of the strata to be obtained and brought to the surface for examination. Coring, however, slows down the speed of boring owing to the increasing amount of time that is required to withdraw each length of core as the hole gets deeper.

Because of this, coring is often employed only when traversing or passing through the strata which actually contains the coal seams. For the other parts of the strata, the steel bits used are fitted with toothed wheels which cut rapidly down through the rocks, the rock fragments being then flushed to the surface by circulating a specially prepared mixture of mud and water through the hollow rods. The debris from the borehole tells its own story of the rocks, and from this the trained geologist can make a complete journal of the bore showing the position of the coals and the estimated thickness of each seam.

The use of bigger and more powerful rigs has enabled greater boring depths and speeds to be attained than was possible in earlier years. A bore sunk recently at Brucefield, near Clackmannan, reached a depth of 4,406 feet in just under thirteen months, while another at Archerbeck, near Canonbie, reached 4,604 feet in fourteen months. By way of comparison, the deep bore sunk at Balfour Mains in Fife just over fifty years ago took five years to reach a depth of 4,534 feet.

CONSTRUCTION OF THE SHAFTS

With reference to shaft construction, it was the practice until some thirty years ago to form a rectangular shaft, the sides being lined and strengthened with strong timber, generally larch. In modern practice, however, the stronger circular-type shaft is preferred as it provides more room for the installation of the power cables, pumping and other equipment; in addition, it allows of better ventilation. Apart from the interruption of the air flow which occurs in a rectangular shaft when the down-going cage is passing the up-coming cage, the volume of air to be circulated in the bigger mines of to-day has grown very considerably, and circular shafts with wide clearance are now indispensable to good mining practice.

The concrete walling, or lining, used in the construction of circular shafts gives added strength and also provides a smooth surface which offers less resistance to the air flow. In large modern collieries this is particularly important on account of the increased volume of air required to provide the higher ventilation standards now demanded.

When sinking through heavily watered strata, operations become extremely difficult for the men working at the bottom of the sinking shaft. To control the water inflow, brine, which is circulated through a series of boreholes, is sometimes used to freeze the strata round the shaft. Another method now more generally used is to inject liquid cement into the strata to seal off the water while sinking is in progress.

In modern practice, the shafts are sunk to the full depth of the workable seams. One or more working " horizons " (or depths) are then selected, at which level roads are driven from the shafts to intersect the coals. The field is then opened out by a series of roads driven in the seam to form a network of underground arteries. The coal is then lowered or transported by conveyor to the main haulage road and loaded into mine cars for transport by

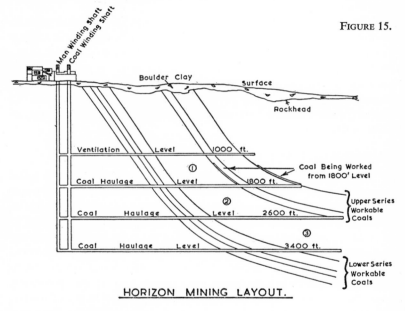

FIGURE 15.

HORIZON MINING LAYOUT.

locomotive to the shaft. The horizon principle is illustrated in the accompanying diagram, showing the rotation of extraction—starting with the upper panel and developing the lower coals later. Panels numbered 1 to 3 are marked; further panels may be laid off as necessary.

DEVELOPMENTS IN VENTILATION PRACTICE

Mechanical ventilators of many different types have been tried out with varying degrees of success over the last 150 years. One of the most successful of the earlier types was the air pump invented by

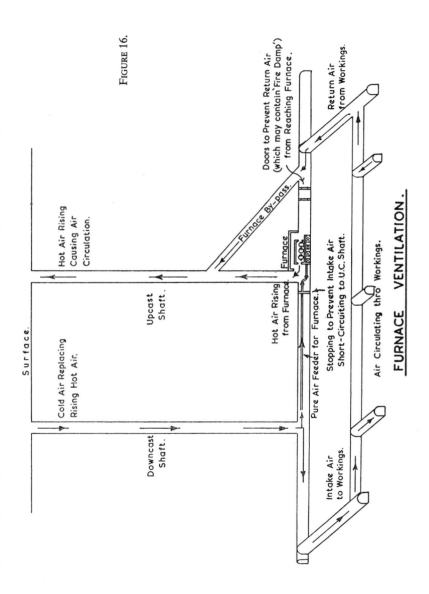

FIGURE 16.

FURNACE VENTILATION.

John Buddle, an eminent North of England engineer. This pump, introduced in 1813, was fitted with a wooden piston five feet square with eight-foot stroke, and was capable of "exhausting", or withdrawing, 6,000 cubic feet of air per minute. It is of interest to note that one of the first mine ventilation fans of which there is any record was installed at a colliery in the Paisley district as far back as 1827. This fan, which was fitted with large vanes similar to those used in winnowing machines, attracted considerable interest.

FIGURE 17.

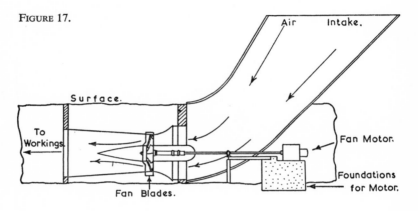

AXIAL FLOW FAN.

From about 1840, attention was mainly directed to the development of the centrifugal type of fan, in which the air enters at the centre and is displaced outwards through the blades at the periphery. There were, of course, various designs of ventilation fans. The sceptical attitude[1] of the industry towards mechanical ventilators persisted to such an extent that the traditional system of ventilation—the underground furnace—was retained in general use until the beginning of the present century. The accompanying figure (No. 16) illustrates the method that was employed in furnace ventilation practice to circulate the fresh air from the surface round the workings and back up the upcast, the main current by-passing the open furnace itself in order to avoid the risk of an explosion should firedamp be present in the mine air.

[1] In Eastern Scotland, there was only one fan of any sort in 1873—*An Economic History of Modern Britain* by J. H. Clapham, Vol. 2, p. 102.

With the axial-flow type fan, which was a later development, the direction of the air flow is unchanged. This gives the axial-flow fan an advantage over the centrifugal type, in which the air flow is sharply diverted, the increased resistance caused thereby resulting in a loss of efficiency. The pitch of the blades, also, is variable with some axial-flow type fans, so that an increased air supply can be

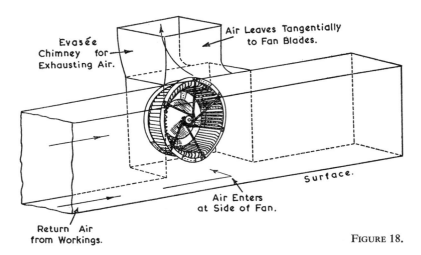

Evasée Chimney for Exhausting Air.

Air Leaves Tangentially to Fan Blades.

Surface.

Air Enters at Side of Fan.

Return Air from Workings.

FIGURE 18.

SIROCCO FAN.

readily obtained. The air inlet, along with the outlet to the atmosphere and the casings of the auxiliary parts in the air passage are streamlined to give an improved flow of air. Figure 17 illustrates the axial-flow fan.

The modern high-capacity fan is a small machine, often less than 12 feet in diameter, when compared with some of the early mechanical ventilators, which sometimes reached 40 feet in diameter. Figure 18 shows a Sirocco fan, widely used before the modern axial-flow type came into use.

In addition to keeping the mine supplied with fresh air and clear of gas, the ventilation system prevents the mine from becoming too hot and difficult to work in. The strata temperatures in Scottish collieries rise by an average of one degree Fahrenheit every 70 feet of depth, while the compression of the air as it is forced down the shaft results in a further increase of one degree Fahrenheit every 182 feet descended. Further, the friction set up by machinery, oxidation, and the exertions of the mineworkers also tend to raise the underground temperatures.

The weight of air entering and leaving the shafts each day is about five or six times the *weight* of coal produced. In some large collieries as much as 500,000 cubic feet of air per minute may be required, equivalent to 26,000 tons of air per day, resulting in a continuous wind velocity of over 1,000 feet per minute in some parts of the main airways.

EARLY FORMS OF UNDERGROUND TRANSPORT

The most primitive form of underground transport used in moving the coal from the hewer's working place to the pit-bottom was, as we saw in Chapter II, the human bearer. The practice of employing women and children to perform this fearful drudgery lasted for nearly 500 years, and only came to an end with the passing of the Act of 1842 (see Chapter VII, p. 91) prohibiting the employment underground of women and girls and of boys under the age of ten.

By the middle of the eighteenth century the use of sledges and four-wheeled vehicles (hutches) drawn by ponies or horses was beginning to ease the burden of the human bearers to some extent, but the introduction of these transport innovations was somewhat spasmodic and desultory. In practically all parts of the Scottish coalfield, bearers were retained in general use for a hundred years or so after ponies or horses had first made their appearance underground. By the time the 1842 Act came into operation, however, the haulage of coal in hutches by men and boys and by ponies was an established system of transport underground. Collieries in the East of Scotland, it would appear, were somewhat slower in replacing the bearers than collieries in the West, the Lanarkshire pits probably being spurred on to improve their transport methods by the growing demand for coal from the iron and other rapidly expanding industries on Clydeside.

The use of self-acting inclined planes, which can be used only in " rise " workings from which coal has to be *lowered* to the shaft bottom, marked another interesting advance in underground transport. Before this system could be employed the degree of inclination on the roadway had to be sufficiently steep to allow the descending load of full hutches from the rise workings to haul up the empty hutches, while the double track that was required involved the construction and maintenance of much wider roadways than were normally used at that period. The system was first described and used about the year 1750, though as far as can be ascertained it was not adopted to any noticeable extent until the nineteenth century. Despite their somewhat limited application, self-acting haulages are still to be found in many of the older Scottish collieries. Where coal is being worked below pit-bottom level—that is, in dip workings—this system cannot, of course, be adopted.

The beginning of the nineteenth century brought one of the most historic of all the changes that have been introduced in underground transport—the use of the steam engine. The form of transport first employed to incorporate this significant development was Direct Rope or Main Rope haulage. Where roadways were not sufficiently steep to serve as self-acting inclines but were steep enough to permit the empty hutches to pull the haulage rope inbye to the dip this system worked admirably—the miner simply detaching the "empties" and clipping the full hutches on to the rope, which was then hauled up by the engine.

Thus it was that the steam engine first came to be used to haul coal underground where the gradient of the roadway was fairly steep; but some thirty years were to pass before similar mechanical means were introduced for haulage purposes on level roads or on roads with gentle gradients. The main reason for this delay was almost certainly the fact that haulage of hutches by hand or by pony was adequate for the satisfactory performance of these lighter duties particularly having regard to the limited knowledge then available about the possibilities of mechanical haulage generally.

It may be noticed, in passing, that one of the first colliery engineers to use a steam engine to haul coal up an underground incline was George Stephenson, known later as a pioneer of the railway locomotive. About the year 1812, when he was the enginewright at Killingworth Colliery in the North of England, Stephenson adapted a pumping engine to haul coal, and extended his system of underground mechanical transport at Killingworth to such an extent that one engine, complete with boiler, was installed no less than

1,500 yards distant from the shaft, the combustion gases and smoke being conveyed in flues to the pit-bottom.

For the transportation of coal along level or undulating roadways neither self-acting nor direct rope haulage was suitable, as these

FIGURE 19.

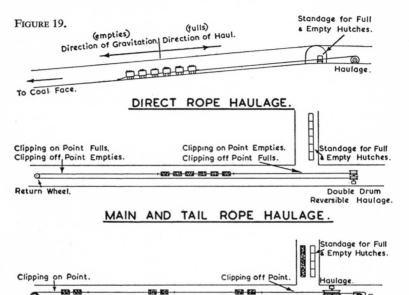

DIRECT ROPE HAULAGE.

MAIN AND TAIL ROPE HAULAGE.

ENDLESS ROPE HAULAGE.

BALANCE ROPE HAULAGE.

could not provide the two-way traction needed under such conditions, whereupon a third system was introduced (about the year 1844), known as Main and Tail Rope haulage, and requiring a single track only. The haulage engine in this case was equipped with two drums, fitted with clutch and brake.

The tail rope was, first of all, carried inbye along the *side* of the track on pulleys, passed round a terminus wheel, and then led back along the *centre* of the haulage road to the pit-bottom to pick up a set or "rake" of empty hutches, to the other end of which was attached the main rope. The tail rope drum was then engaged and the " empties" hauled inbye, dragging the main rope behind them. At the end of their journey, the empty hutches were detached and returned to the working faces, while the main rope picked up the "fulls" and was hauled back to the pit-bottom by the second drum, this time dragging the tail rope behind. The disadvantage of this system lay in the fact that on long distance it did not provide a steady service of hutches in either direction, and, therefore, tended to make filling and winding operations somewhat irregular. On short undulating roads the system is still popular.

About the year 1844, also, another system of haulage free from the disadvantage just mentioned was introduced. This was known as Endless Rope haulage, in which an endless rope travels continuously between the pit-bottom and the loading points inbye. With this type of haulage the hutches can be clipped on as they arrive, which ensures that the "empties" are kept moving constantly and continuously to the coalface to be filled, while the loaded hutches are moving with equal regularity into the pit-bottom to keep the winding going steadily. Another advantage of Endless Rope haulage is that the load on the haulage rope itself can be distributed more evenly. This system is still in common use, though within the last few years the use of underground locomotives, running on level roads, and capable of hauling a heavy train of mine cars, has been demonstrated to be the most efficient of all forms of main-road transport underground. The latter form of underground transport is now standard for all new and reconstructed collieries on account of the large tonnage it can handle and its low running cost.

The pattern of underground transport which was emerging about 1850 has, broadly speaking, persisted with various improvements but no fundamental change until the present time. One exception must be made to this general statement, however, and that is the introduction of mechanical conveyors to transport the coal along the longwall faces, and from the face to the main haulage roads, developments of far-reaching importance which began just over fifty years ago. The earliest form of mechanical conveyor was the scraper type, introduced in 1902, consisting of an endless steel chain carrying

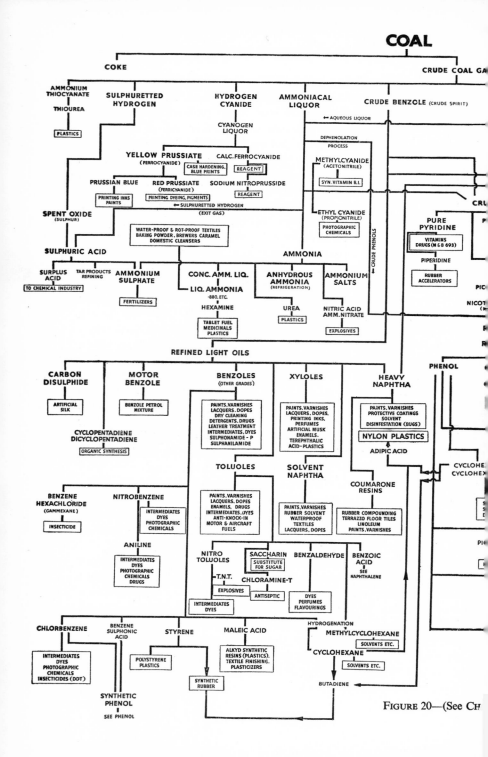

FIGURE 20—(See Ch

CTS OF THE MANUFACTURE OF GAS & COKE FROM COAL
USES AND MANUFACTURED DERIVATIVES ARE ALSO INCLUDED

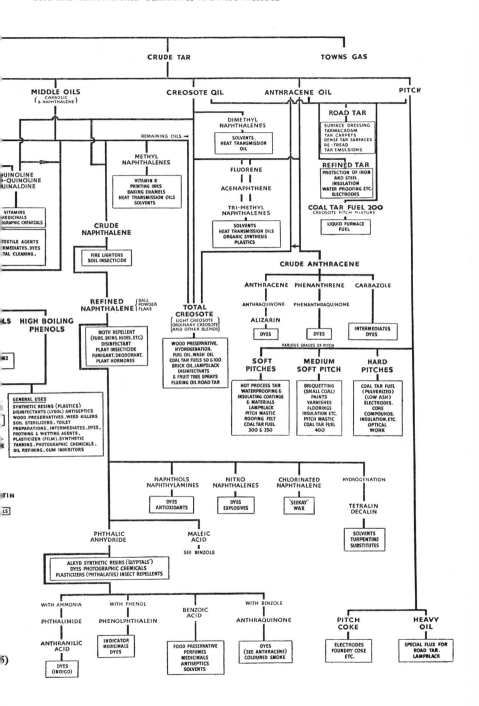

a series of scrapers, which deliver the coal along a steel trough resting on the floor or pavement.

The jigger or shaker conveyor was put on the market just before World War I and was first introduced into this country by Mavor and Coulson, the initial order going to the Lothian Coal Company Limited. This conveyor, by virtue of its simple construction gained considerable support and was widely used for many years. The roadway conveyor now in most common use, however, is the belt or band conveyor. Its advantages in steep gradients, smooth running and silent operation have given the belt conveyor first place. On longwall faces where the coal is power-loaded, the belt conveyor has been replaced by the armoured chain conveyor.

The smooth, flexible and speedy transport which the modern conveyor provides has given it a high place in the operational network which is so essential to modern machine mining. To begin with, mechanical conveyors were not thought to have a wide application outwith thin seams where space restrictions rendered the free action of the miner impossible. It was soon realised, however, that the use of gate loading conveyors in conjunction with face conveyors was not only feasible but could materially assist coal production, and later their application was extended successfully to trunk roads inbye.

The introduction of conveyors, retarded at first by the reluctance of both management and men to appreciate the intrinsic merits of this form of transport, particularly in low or narrow roads, has eased the labour of the collier and helped to speed up production. Conveyors have been widely used in Scotland for many years, and, indeed, until quite recently England lagged well behind her partner in the matter of mechanical conveying of coal. This was probably due, in part at least, to the higher proportion of thin and steeply graded seams which Scotland found herself obliged to work. Indeed, without the assistance of this transport innovation many of the thin seams worked in Scotland would have had to be abandoned as uneconomic.

MACHINE MINING

The way in which mining engineers finally succeeded—after a long struggle against the forces of nature and with the help of others not directly engaged in the industry—in reducing the task of coal-hewing to a mechanical art never fails to arouse interest. When and where did the story begin? It is not possible to say but we know that as early as 1768 a machine had been invented which swung the pick into the coal. The head was mounted on a special frame and affixed to a "swinging arm", a series of gears and levers energised by the miner himself being used to drive the pick into the coal. This method had its limitations since the machine could only be cranked or rotated by one or two men at most, and in circumstances where freedom of action was heavily restricted. A horse-driven pick machine, too, was used, but again with only limited success.

Gradually it became apparent that a machine simulating the action of the ordinary miner's pick, however ingeniously constructed, was not the answer, and attention turned to finding some other way of cutting the coal. Thus, about 1843, a coal-cutting circular saw was patented and introduced, and although different designs were tried out, lack of power other than hand-propulsion again blocked the way to success. Before going on to mention a Scottish invention which had a much greater success than any of the "machines" noted so far, it is only right to state that a number of the mechanical inventions mentioned in this Chapter were of English origin.

In 1864 an important milestone was passed, for in that year William Baird and Company, Coatbridge, brought out the famous "Gartsherrie" machine. This was the first chain machine ever used to cut coal and the first heavy mechanically operated coal-cutter to be introduced into a Scottish mine—namely, Baird's Lochwood Pit at Cuilhill, Bargeddie, near Glasgow. The first of these machines was driven by a single-cylinder engine, the motive power being compressed air. An improved version of this machine was shown at the Philadelphia Exhibition of 1876. The Americans appreciated its possibilities and made the fullest use of it in their subsequent researches. Many of the features of the "Gartsherrie" machine are embodied in the modern coal-cutter. A model, the original one used by Bairds in 1864, can be seen in the Royal Scottish Museum, Edinburgh (see Plate 12, facing p. 81).

At the time when the first coal-cutters were introduced the poor quality of metals available to the makers, apart altogether from the mechanical limitations of the machines themselves, seriously affected performance. At that period, steelmaking was in its infancy and alloy steels were unknown. In the early 1850's, Robert F. Mushet of Dalkeith discovered and used the ferro-manganese formula for the making of steel, the method now, of course, in universal use. Mushet's discoveries, patented in 1856, are thought by many authorities to transcend even Bessemer's famous contribution, the converter. Robert Mushet was also the first to produce alloy steel, but this was many years after he had discovered and expounded the secret of steel-making.

The "Gartsherrie" machine illustrates the point made about inferior metals, for we have it on good authority that William Baird and Company ceased to produce or use this machine because of the time lost through breakdowns, mainly of the chains, for which (and for the picks also) no metal was available tough enough to stand up to the abrasion. This may partly account for the fact that the bar and disc types of coal-cutters were for many years thereafter preferred to the chain-type.

The chain machine, however, continued to be developed and improved in the United States, and was later re-introduced into this country. The picks, which were attached to a moving endless cutter chain mounted on a jib, excavated the bottom six inches of the seam at floor level for a distance of about $4\frac{1}{2}$ feet into the coalface, a single cutter being able to undercut a face of approximately 200 yards length in six hours.

PUMPING TECHNIQUES

In a previous chapter reference was made to the increasing severity of water problems arising from the working of deeper seams. The first attempt to introduce pumping machinery was made by Savery in 1698 when he employed the principle of the condensed steam vacuum to draw the water up to the engine, then using steam pressure to force it above the engine. This principle is still in use to-day.

Newcomen's atmospheric steam engine, invented about 1705, was an improvement on Savery's pump, being fitted with a separate cylinder and piston. Steam was introduced on one side of the piston and then condensed. The vacuum thus created allowed the atmospheric pressure on the opposite side to force the piston before it, and raise the rods attached to the engine. The Newcomen pump remained in general use until superseded by more efficient types using the Watt pumping engine. For the greater part of the eighteenth century, therefore, pumping facilities were limited; many mines and collieries became water-logged and had to be abandoned, with heavy loss to their owners.

Watt's original engines had been used to replace the Newcomen suction-type in use in the tin mines of Cornwall, and the subsequent improvements that were made centred mainly round these "Cornish" pumps. The success of the Cornish pump was due to its ability to exert a positive pressure on the top side of the piston while simultaneously creating a vacuum on the bottom side of the vertical cylinder. The piston's upstroke was made by the weight or "pull" of the pump rods themselves.

Owing to the heavy and complicated system of rods and bucket pumps in the shaft, with their Cornish beam-type engines aboveground, serious maintenance difficulties arose, especially in the deeper mines. Broken rods were a source of serious damage, and led to the development of a compact direct-acting high-speed steam-driven pump located in the pit bottom and requiring only a pipe column in the shaft itself.

Towards the close of the last century came a rapid expansion in the use of electrical power. Its introduction heralded further changes in the design of pumping equipment. Water cylinder multi-ram pumps were at first a popular choice because of their greater continuity of water flow and reduced shock to pipe joints and the other mechanical parts of the pump. Ram or piston-type pumps have continued to be used widely during the present century, but the modern centrifugal pump is now preferred, chiefly on account of its greater suitability for electric drive.

WINDING DEVELOPMENTS

Two outstanding advances of the period were the introduction of the flat wire rope in 1840 and the introduction the following year of high-pressure steam winding engines; previous to this time, all winding ropes were made of hemp. These developments made it then possible to wind much greater tonnages and paved the way for the substantially increased colliery outputs which followed shortly afterwards.

The new engines were first installed at some of the pits in the Airdrie district of Lanarkshire, their subsequent application raising the winding capacity of collieries from around 250 tons to about 600 tons per day within a very short period. By 1850 the cheaper

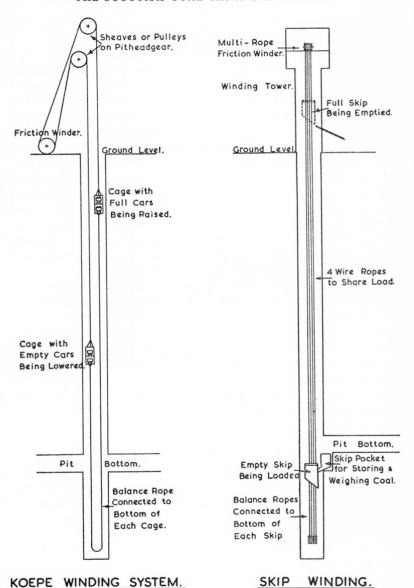

KOEPE WINDING SYSTEM. SKIP WINDING.

FIGURE 21.

(*Figures in Chapter V drawn by R. Longmore*)

and more durable round wire rope had been invented and introduced, though the flat rope did not finally disappear until about the turn of the century.

Many refinements and changes have taken place with engines, ropes, drums, shaft mountings and other winding gear in the last hundred years. One of the chief problems was to overcome the increase in the "moment of inertia" when starting the wind from the pit-bottom, due to the increasing depths of many pits and the weight of the long rope. One method of solving the problem was the development of the Koepe system of winding which uses a friction pulley at the surface instead of a drum. Over this pulley passes an endless rope to which the cages or skips are attached. Now that the earlier difficulty of "slip" has been overcome this method of winding has returned to favour (*see* Fig. 21).

In the latest type of winding equipment for big shafts of between 18 and 24 feet diameter, using powerful A.C. electric winding motors, the coal is either wound to the surface in cages holding mine cars of 2 to 3 tons capacity (four cars per wind) or in skips of 10 tons capacity and over. These winders can raise this weight of coal from 2,500 feet in about 40 seconds.

The loading and unloading of the mine cars or skips is now a fully mechanised operation at new collieries. A substantial saving of manpower is thus effected, one man in the pit-bottom and another at the surface being all that is required. As the signalling and winding controls are interlocked with the switches which control the mechanical decking arrangements above and below ground the possibility of accidents is virtually eliminated. These modern methods offer a striking contrast to the former methods in which many men were needed to push and load and unload the hutches. Where hutches are still in use these modern systems can, of course, be applied.

Experiments have been undertaken to prove whether the hydraulic transportation of coal through pipes to the surface is feasible and to what extent this form of raising coal might be suitable to replace the more conventional systems of winding already described. The experiments, undertaken by the National Coal Board at Woodend Colliery, Armadale, have shown that coal can be raised to the surface in metal pipes along with the water pumped up the shaft, but whether the system is sufficiently practicable to be economic it is too early to say at this stage.

DEVELOPMENTS IN THE APPLICATION OF POWER

Because of the arduous and difficult nature of the work involved in recovering coal from the recesses of the earth's crust, more time and effort have been expended in attempts to provide suitable machines and suitable plant in mines to assist the workman than is the case in industry generally. This is one of the reasons why mining is able to provide so much material of interest regarding the pioneering efforts of the mechanical engineer during the last two centuries. Because of its dangers and complexities, mining has exercised the minds of many able men anxious to render what assistance they could. It is certain that James Watt had the centuries-old water problem of the mines very much at heart as he laboured to develop the steam engine. One of the first, if not the first, of his new engines was used about 1768 to pump water at a Scottish mine near Kinneil House where he was staying at the time.

The motive power used in mining has been supplied from three main sources—steam, compressed air and electricity. Steam, which has played the dominant rôle, was first applied to operate a pumping engine invented by Savery in 1698. In his book describing his invention Savery used the title *The Miners' Friend*, connoting the close connection of mining with this historic invention. It is note-worthy, too, that George Stephenson worked as a colliery engineer, or engine-wright, for many years before turning his attention to the railways with which his name is more popularly associated.

By 1850, steam power was already in general use for pumping, haulage and winding purposes. In these early days it was not un-common to install the engines and boilers underground. The danger of an explosion of firedamp, however, led to the boilers being sited on the surface and the steam piped down the shaft to operate the pumps and haulages. This system of power transmission then became fairly general and was retained in use at many collieries until not long before World War I, and in a few isolated cases until just prior to World War II. Heat losses in transmission, however, proved heavy and to obviate this, underground haulages were frequently operated by ropes or rods from the surface, a practice which was still in occasional use until after World War I and in one or two exceptional cases until shortly after World War II.

Though the steam engines used in and about the collieries over the last century or more had been improved progressively and

80

PLATE 10—A.B. FIFTEEN LONG-WALL COAL-CUTTER fitted with mushroom jib
and arranged for flight-loading.

PLATE 11—A.B. MECO-MOORE CUTTER LOADER. Produces a relatively high
proportion of large coal.

PLATE 12 — GARTSHERRIE MACHINE.

brought to a high state of efficiency, the use of steam presented certain inherent problems, due to heat losses arising from condensation and leakage between the surface boiler and the engines underground, many at points a considerable distance from the pit bottom. As a result of this, the use of compressed air to drive coal-cutters, pumps and haulages was widely employed, the transmission losses with compressed air being generally much lighter than with steam.

Compressed air was first used in British mining at Govan Colliery, Glasgow, where an air compressor was installed in 1849 to supply the motive power to operate haulage and pumping machinery situated underground about half-a-mile inbye. The engine operated on the beam principle, having the steam cylinder at one end of the beam and the crank at the other, with two single-acting air compressors intermediate. The air was compressed to 30 pounds per square inch, and passed into a central receiver, from which it was transmitted inbye in cast iron pipes.

Although the installation at Govan Colliery appears to have been successful, taking into account the elementary stage reached at that time in the design of mechanical equipment generally, little further headway in the application of compressed-air power took place for many years afterwards. The "Gartsherrie" coal-cutter produced in 1864 was air driven, but it is difficult to quote other examples. Smyth's *Coal and Coal Mining*, published in 1866, has no reference to compressed air, from which it may be inferred that it played little or no part in coal mining up to that time.

During the construction of the Mt. Cenis and St Gothard tunnels through the Alps in the third quarter of last century compressed air proved its worth and mining interest in the potentialities of compressed air revived. By this time, also, makers of air compressors had made considerable headway, and by about 1880–90 the stage had been reached when the two main problems associated with compressed air—namely, the rise in temperature during compression and the freezing of the exhaust ports of the motors—had been measurably reduced.

One of the main uses of compressed air was to drive the new coal-cutters. The scope which this development offered is reflected in the fact that in 1900 only 3 per cent. of the coal produced in Scotland was machine cut—the percentage for England being even lower. By 1920 the Scottish figure was 34 per cent. and the

English figure 13 per cent., while the position now shows that both countries have reached approximately the same figure, about 87 per cent. Until around the early 'thirties most of the coal-cutters were air-driven, but thereafter the use of electrically-operated machines became standard practice.

ELECTRIFICATION OF MINING MACHINERY

In 1831 Michael Faraday succeeded in demonstrating how a steady current of electricity could be induced by revolving an electric conductor in a magnetic field so that it cut across the lines of magnetic force. In this discovery lay the foundation of one of the greatest industrial and social revolutions the world has ever seen. Though the electric generator, which enables mechanical power to be converted into electric power, was being manufactured by 1870, this new form of power had no appreciable industrial application until about 1890.

The mining industry was among the first to encourage the use of electricity, and to Earnock Colliery, Hamilton, fell the distinction of introducing electric lighting successfully into mining, the first mains lighting system being installed underground at this pit about 1881.[1] The firm which carried out the work, Messrs D. and G. Graham, a Scottish firm, were also responsible for the lighting installed in Lord Kelvin's house at Glasgow University.

In the early days, the danger arising from open sparking tended to restrict the use of electricity and electrical equipment, but in 1912 special rules were framed and steps taken to ensure that all electrical apparatus to be used where firedamp might be present must be specially protected and carry the official FLP (flameproof) stamp. From that time, the range of electrical equipment of approved type and design has been expanded steadily and subjected to rigorous test to ensure that only FLP equipment of the highest standard is used.

All electrical equipment for use underground, particularly the motors, cable joints and switchgear, must be constructed and protected so as to prevent open-sparking, and must be of robust design suitable to withstand the stress and strain which mining

---

[1] An electrically-driven coal-cutter was supplied by Messrs King, Brown and Company, Rosebank Electric Works, Edinburgh, to Messrs R. and J. Durie, Elphinstone Colliery, Tranent, early in 1891, at a cost of £245.

conditions impose. FLP equipment, due to the skill and experience of the makers, is virtually foolproof as well as flameproof.

Though compressed air is still used for drilling, pumping, coal-cutting and conveying at many collieries, electric power is the most convenient and the most efficient prime mover and the new modern collieries which the National Coal Board are constructing are all designed to use electricity almost exclusively. With electricity, the interlocking of plant and equipment can be readily secured to prevent machinery being moved until everything is in order to start in complete safety. For example, it is now becoming the practice to install fully automatic winding in which the margin for human error or mechanical error is practically eliminated.

CONCLUSION

It would be difficult to single out any fundamental discovery during the last 100 years which has impacted on mining to the same extent as the work of Watt or Faraday, but the application of mechanical principles has been extended so far in all directions during the past century as to revolutionise completely the science of mining as we know it to-day. The progress made with power-loading machinery is a good example of this. These machines (*see* plates 8, 10, 11, 17, 18 and 20) cut and load the coal mechanically, some being ingenious adaptations of the conventional coal-cutter, while others mark a completely independent engineering approach to coal-winning.

The coal plough, for example, literally slices the coal off the face by sharp blades set after the manner of a plough share. Another machine, the Anderton Shearer Loader, has a pick-studded re-volving drum as the cutting medium, whilst the Trepanner acts like a continuous boring machine. These machines work on what is known in mining circles as the "continuous principle". Instead of having as at present a somewhat cumbersome three-shift system (two shifts for preparatory work and a third shift for the stripping or winning of the coal), the men coming on shift can take over the machine on any part of the face. On continuous mining faces, also, the preparatory work can be carried out independent of the coal-getting shift, which makes for much greater productivity and efficient working.

These new power-loading techniques have not yet reached the stage where they could replace conventional longwall mining methods entirely. Physical conditions vary widely and many of the new machines are fairly selective; as time goes on the scope of power-loading machines will no doubt increase. Special conveying and propping techniques have been introduced to suit the new power-loading methods, the conveyors being moved forward by the use of hydraulic rams instead of being laboriously dismantled and re-erected as in conventional mining practice.

That electricity—already playing an essential part in the operations of the colliery, both above and below ground—will find fresh fields of usefulness in the future is beyond doubt. The possibilities of this have already been demonstrated by electrical engineers attached to the industry. For communication purposes the ordinary "walkie-talkie" apparatus is useless underground as the message fades away within less than 50 yards, but this difficulty has been overcome by the use of a metallic conductor which enables the signals to be "guided" along the underground passages for a distance of $1\frac{1}{2}$ miles without loss of signal. A special conductor is unnecessary, any cable or pipe in the roadway being sufficient.

As already indicated, the signalling and winding switches can be interlocked with the mechanical decking mechanism; one day this may be taken a step further as it is now possible to initiate the wind automatically by " counting " the mine cars electrically as they enter the cage. Further refinements in winding automation are gradually being brought into play by the use of the photo-electric cell. In one application the cell throws a beam of light on to the shaft area; should there be any obstruction the light beam is interrupted and the relay circuit operates—bringing movement to a standstill instantly.

One would not go so far as to suggest that the electronic " brain " will one day take over control of all important mining operations, but its use as an additional safety precaution presents distinct possibilities. Thus electrical equipment, at one time regarded as dangerous in mining, may bring to the industry the means of creating a fool-proof safety technique which will reduce still further the hazards of mining.

In many instances, electricity has already put to flight the smoke and grime at one time characteristic of most collieries; has revolutionised the design of plant and machinery, and has raised the operating efficiency of the collieries to a level which could not have been achieved in any other way.

CHAPTER VI

THE INDUSTRY NATIONALISED

WORLD WAR I AND WORLD WAR II inevitably interrupted and seriously retarded the technical progress of the Coal Industry, but the economic depression which hung heavily over the nation during the dull years between did more damage and sapped the strength and efficiency of the mining industry far more. Short-time working and unemployment caused hundreds of thousands of men to leave the mines altogether, while those who remained in the industry had imprinted on their minds a memory of hard times which the reformed and improved conditions of later years have scarcely yet eradicated.

During the period covered by these events—that is from 1914 until 1945—the amount of new capital that was invested in the industry was totally inadequate either to sustain its strength or prevent a grave decline in its productive assets. In an extractive industry like coal mining such neglect must bring disastrous consequences, and the Report of the Technical Advisory Committee in 1945 made no attempt to disguise the state of inefficiency or the parlous loss of productive capacity which the industry had sustained. In the following year Parliament decided to place the industry under public ownership.

When the Scottish Division of the National Coal Board took over control on 1st January 1947, they assumed responsibility for 275 Scottish mines previously owned and managed by no less than 120 separate colliery undertakings. Included were 79 small mines working scattered " pockets " of coal which the Divisional Board decided to leave under the direction of their previous owners, to whom they granted a special operating licence. All other mines, numbering 196, came under the direct management of the Board at Vesting Date.

On being subjected to a searching examination, more than half of the collieries were found to be in an advanced state of physical and economic decline on account of their age and the exhaustion of their workable coal reserves: all these mines, it was computed, would have to be closed by 1965 at latest and many of them long before that date. The Board's assessment of the situation has been amply confirmed by subsequent events, many of the collieries in this category now having closed, with the others following closely behind. In their final, declining years these units were not only incurring heavy financial losses but were also extremely wasteful of manpower.

The loss of output from the closure of these old collieries—many of them dating from last century—was estimated to amount to nearly 7,000,000 annual tons of saleable coal. Faced by a peremptory closure programme of such formidable size, the Divisional Board set to at once to frame and carry through a programme of large-scale development, the task being not only to replace the heavy output loss arising from closures, especially in the declining Lanarkshire Coalfield, but also to raise the Scottish annual output from its post-war level of just over 20,000,000 tons to about 30,000,000 tons.

Pending the preparation and execution of comprehensive plans for the reconstruction of many of the existing collieries and the sinking of new deep pits in the developing coalfields—a task which would inevitably take years to complete—the Board adopted vigorous measures to relieve the immediate supply position by pressing forward normal colliery development work and constructing some sixty new surface drift mines. These mines were essentially short-life projects, designed to recover " pockets " of shallow coals in various parts of the coalfield. Equipped with modern high-speed machinery and specially designed underground haulage systems, the new drift mines proved most successful, some of them achieving outputs ranging from fifty to seventy hundredweights per manshift worked.

It was realised by her mining engineers that the real solution for Scotland's shrinking coal output problem lay in the reconstruction and modernisation of as many of her existing collieries as could justify the heavy expenditure that would be necessary to bring them to a state of full technical efficiency, coupled with the construction of more than a dozen large new fittings to develop the unworked and rich reserves still lying in the deeper parts of the Scottish Coalfield. These two programmes have entailed an enormous amount of detailed and careful planning, particularly having regard to the peculiar mining hazards and risks that had to be faced—difficulties from which other industries are quite free.

A further complication was the scarcity of men with the requisite knowledge and experience of modern large-scale colliery construction and development since little work of this nature had been undertaken, as the reader may have gathered from a previous reference, for many years prior to this time.

Let us consider, first, the pits selected by the Divisional Board for comprehensive reconstruction and modernisation. These were pits which, although they had substantial coal reserves, could not be run in a fully efficient manner in their existing condition, because they were handicapped by lack of winding capacity, poor underground roads and transport, inadequate depth of shafts, and so on. In all, some forty pits were found to qualify for a complete overhaul, the great majority being situated in the newer parts of the Scottish Coalfield. Once each pit's particular problems had been analysed, no time was lost in getting to work to resolve them. Where necessary, shafts have been deepened and re-equipped with powerful electric winders and bigger cages or skips; underground roadways have been constructed to accommodate modern haulage systems (locomotives and mine cars); pit-bottoms have been extended and rebuilt, and automatic decking plant and machinery installed. Many other new features have been incorporated as well, such as new coal cleaning plants, additional welfare facilities, bigger sidings, and increased power supplies arranged—in a word, these reconstructed pits are virtually new pits. In this way, substantial labour savings have already been effected, while the average output increase from this group of collieries will be of the order of 50 per cent., not to mention their greatly increased productivity in general.

The planning and construction of some fifteen large collieries to develop the deep coals of Fife, Lothians, Ayrshire and the upper reaches of the Firth of Forth was undoubtedly the most difficult and the most rewarding part of the whole Scottish programme—a programme, incidentally, much heavier than that undertaken by any other Division in Great Britain.

From these great new fittings, when they have been fully developed, will flow the major proportion of the output increase urgently needed. It is also worthy of note that nearly half of the new collieries possess sufficient reserves of coal to enable them to sustain their operations at full production strength for the next hundred years, and in some cases for even longer than that.

The new collieries have been designed to produce up to ten times more coal than was previously produced in a pit of average size. This is because the more readily accessible coal seams have been largely exhausted and much deeper reserves must now be proved and worked in future. In 1947, the average depth of mining operations in Scotland was about 900 feet, but the new pits have had to be sunk to depths of 2000 to 3000 feet, or even more.

This change in depth posed a fundamental technical and economic problem. In these altered circumstances, the new colliery must be designed and equipped to produce not less than about three to four thousand tons of coal, or more, each working day in order to provide a mining unit of economic size. Great new circular shafts, lined with concrete and reinforced with steel, have had to be constructed, as well as spacious new roadways driven through stone for long distances, while for efficient winding from the greater depth powerful electric winders have had to be installed. It has been necessary, of course, to install other mining plant and equipment on a commensurate scale.

The new collieries, with their tall winding towers, present a picture of dignity and elegance conspicuously absent from the rather dingy, exposed and untidy-looking pit-heads of the past. In grouping the various buildings, the Board's architects have produced an arrangement in keeping with contemporary standards of industrial design—an arrangement, too, which has considerably improved the operational efficiency of the lay-out.

With perhaps as many as two to three thousand men going on and off duty daily, it was essential that the surface buildings—such as the pit-head baths, canteen, medical centre, car hall, coal preparation plant and administrative offices—should be laid out in the proper sequence to avoid congestion and inconvenience at surge periods, and this has been done. For the convenience of the workmen, the buildings and corridors have been linked together to give continuous cover from the time the men arrive until they leave again for home at the end of their shift.

The modern colliery has become what at one time seemed impossible—a landmark of arresting interest, in close harmony with its surroundings, and flanked with shrubs and lawns any landscape gardener might be proud of!

The National Coal Board have not only undertaken to restore coal output but have also installed the finest and safest plant available in order to raise the productivity of its collieries to the highest standard technically possible. Many additional welfare services have been provided, and, given the co-operation of the mineworkers, it should be possible to say that the money spent to implement the National Coal Board's vast investment programme for the Scottish Coal Industry—a sum which may well be in excess of £200,000,000—has been wisely laid out.

Plate 13—Killoch Colliery, near Ochiltree, Ayrshire, under construction.

Plate 14—An aerial view of the new Kinneil Colliery, Bo'ness, West Lothian.

PLATE 15—DRILLING FOR COAL AT
Boring Tower in the Firth of Fo

PLATE 16.

Operator removing section of the core
from the bore pipe.

PLATE 17—MINING MACHINERY.   Coal plough at the coalface.

(*See text, page 83*)

PLATE 18—MINING MACHINERY. Trepanner; also self-advancing chocks and panzer conveyor.

Plate 19—Mining Machinery. Long-wall coal-cutter at the coalface.

Plate 20—Anderton Shearer Loader, showing the cutting head and plough attachment (p. 83).

CHAPTER VII

MINING HAZARDS AND THE DEVELOPMENT OF SAFETY PRECAUTIONS

THOUGH MANY OF YOU may never have been down a coal mine, you will probably have pictured some of the dangers and difficulties that face the miner who has to work in a narrow confined space far below ground. Not only has he to get out the coal, an arduous enough task in itself, but he must also ensure that the roof overhead is securely supported. As the coal seams often lie immediately below comparatively soft roof strata, such as blaes, which would quickly collapse unless promptly and adequately supported, the miner must always be on the alert against this danger.

It should, perhaps, be explained that while roof pressures are heavy, and must be carefully controlled, the pressure exerted is considerably less than the equivalent of the full dead-weight of the strata between the underground workings and the surface, part of the strain being taken by the rock beds themselves. In addition, the stone packs and other steel or wood supports erected by the miners gradually take the pressure. Nevertheless, the load on the props which the miner sets to support his working place may be from ten to twenty tons, and in some cases may reach a pressure of forty tons per prop. Props made of steel, or of strong timber such as larch, which have a " breaking point " well above the pressures normally encountered, are generally used, and afford the necessary safety.

Over a period of many million years earth pressures have played an essential part in the process whereby the original vegetable matter ultimately became converted into coal—a subject of great interest to chemists and geologists, and one which even to-day has not been entirely explained. The process by which coal was formed, and in which pressure undoubtedly exerted a definite influence, has resulted in the production of a dangerous gas called methane which is released during mining operations. The oxygen in the ventilating air current circulated during mining operations sometimes leads to the production of other dangerous gases, which will be referred to presently. Thus, stringent precautions must be taken to avoid danger from noxious or inflammable gases.

To these gas hazards must be added another—coal dust. This is produced in considerable quantity in the course of coal extraction, coal being an extremely friable substance. The operations mainly responsible for the creation of coal dust are coal-cutting, shot-firing, filling and loading. In good mining practice, the aim is to prevent the coal dust that is inevitably formed from becoming airborne, and later we shall see the steps now taken to control this danger. Stone dust, too, is a serious danger to health; this is formed when cutting or driving through stone or when the " ripping " or removal of stone is necessary to make way for further coal production.

There are various ways in which mine gases and mine dusts can affect the safety or health of the mineworker. The presence of one gas (fire-damp) may, under certain conditions, give rise to a serious explosion, either in combination with coal dust, in which case the results are even more violent, or unassisted. Other gases either asphyxiate or poison. Stone dust, particularly fine stone dust, may gain access to and seriously damage the lungs. In order, therefore, to obviate these risks the most rigorous regulations have been laid down for the proper conduct of all mining operations. This Chapter sets forth, in brief outline, the sustained effort that has been made to bring these mining hazards under control and eliminate them as far as is humanly possible.

In studying the records of the industry with regard to health and safety precautions, one cannot fail to appreciate the extraordinary advance that has taken place in our knowledge of this vast and complex subject and the comparatively recent origin of a considerable part of this knowledge. Management and men alike share the credit for this achievement, though it should in fairness be said that many of the problems and dangers which have beset the industry over the centuries could not have been resolved without the co-operation and help of the scientists, physicists and chemists who have devoted themselves unsparingly to this urgent and rewarding task.

Reviewed in the light of the voluminous legislation since passed, it may surprise to learn that when the nineteenth century opened —and for many years thereafter—there was no Act of Parliament or statutory measure of any kind in force for the protection of the miners against the grim hazards of their calling. The Coal Mines Act of 1842 was the first legislative step that was taken to enable the State to exercise some direct control in this all-important matter, though the primary object of the new Act was not the promotion of mining safety but the reform of abuses connected with the employment of women and children underground.

For many years prior to the passing of this historic measure, private and public opinion had been gradually crystallising in favour of Parliamentary action—not only to stop the employment of women and children underground but also to check the heavy loss of life and injury from explosions and other serious accidents. Thus, Lord Ashley's Bill, which became law in 1842, contained a section providing for the appointment of inspectors. Powers of underground inspection, however, were so restricted that they were never, in fact, exercised. However, a new principle, Government inspection, had emerged. Parliament had at last decided to take a direct interest in mining safety. Under the Act, the minimum age for winding engine-men was fixed at 15! The fundamental change of polity initiated by this measure—namely, the duty of the State to intervene and lay down regulations for the safe conduct of colliery operations— gave great encouragement to the Trade Union movement of those early days, and soon Parliament was being pressed for still more effective action.

Three years later, Government Commissioners were appointed to inquire into the dangers arising from mine gases, and in their Report published in 1846 it was recommended that working plans of all mines must be submitted for registration in order that a central register might be kept for future reference. The Com-missioners also recommended that a centrally controlled inspectorate of mines be established with headquarters in London. The new inspectors were to be made responsible for the supervision of mining safety, and were to be given unrestricted powers to inspect the workings underground.

A Private Member's Bill embodying these and other proposals— the cost of which was to be financed by a levy of $\frac{1}{4}$d. per ton on coal—was presented to Parliament, but failed to get sufficient support and was dropped. Yet another Bill, to prohibit the use of naked lights and gunpowder in fiery (gassy) mines, had also to be dropped for lack of support.

However, in 1850, the Government brought in and passed a Bill of its own. Though this Act fell far short of giving the inspectors the necessary powers to deal effectively with safety problems it did empower them to collect information about accidents. This proved extremely useful in focusing public attention on the dangerous position which still continued in the mines.

The new measure, an Act for the Inspection of Coal Mines in

Great Britain, introduced another legislative principle of far-reaching importance—namely, the right of the State to impose statutory rules and regulations for the promotion of safety in mines. The inspectors were now given the right to institute legal proceedings against anyone infringing the rules and recommendations formulated for the safe conduct of the mines. All fatal accidents from then on had to be reported immediately to the Home Office. The Act also provided for the preparation and registration of correct mine plans.

When this measure expired in 1855, a new Act was passed, which, notwithstanding certain deficiencies, deserves mention in respect that it prescribed for the first time a set of general safety rules and required each colliery to draw up its own special rules and have them approved by the Home Office. Two further Acts, passed in 1860 and 1862 respectively, finally brought the law on the subject of mining safety approximately into line with the best mining practice at that time. In 1862 it was made obligatory to provide each mine or colliery with at least two exits. Ten years later, an Act was passed containing two important mining reforms which gave much satisfaction. It was laid down that every colliery and mine must be managed by a person holding a certificate of competency obtained by State examination. The same Act also conferred on the mineworkers the right to appoint their own representatives to inspect the mine.

With that brief account of the beginnings of safety legislation in this country we must leave the subject, limitations of space preventing us from tracing the course of the formidable volume of legislation subsequently enacted to expand and strengthen safety regulations further. Stage by stage successive Governments have extended the mining safety code as fresh knowledge and additional experience became available, and that procedure will continue as long as coal is worked in this country.

Let us turn back then and look a little more closely at some of the principal dangers associated with coal mining, examine the way in which our predecessors, notwithstanding the limited technical and scientific data available, tackled these problems, and appraise the hard-won success which attended their efforts.

One incident that must have given the industry great encouragement during the early years of last century was the production of the Davy safety lamp in 1815. And this is how it came about. A company of gentlemen, including representatives from the medical and legal professions, the Church, and the peerage, had banded themselves together two years previously to try and solve the age-long problem of underground explosions and other serious mining accidents. It was named the " Committee in Sunderland for the Preventing of Accidents in Coal Mines ". In furtherance of its objectives, the Committee invited the famous scientist, Sir Humphry Davy, then working at the Royal Institution in London, to meet the members and take part in their deliberations. This was one of the wisest decisions ever taken, for at the end of two years' hard work Sir Humphry had found an answer to one of mining's major problems. Though his discovery did not provide the complete answer to the menace of fire-damp, it marked a decisive turning point in the battle against this dangerous gas, but many years were to elapse before the more efficient and safer lamps which superseded it were invented.

Dangerous gases have ever been the miners' most implacable enemy. The chemical properties and the principles which governed the behaviour of these mine gases baffled the industry and the scientists for centuries, particularly ignitions in which coal dust also was involved. Indeed, some of the secrets which underlay the behaviour of dangerous concentrations of mine gases and mine dusts were only revealed during the latter part of the nineteenth century. Men and women, and even children, had thus been obliged for many centuries to work in poorly ventilated and ill-lit collieries surrounded by these dangers because no one understood their nature, and could not, therefore, suggest or provide effective means of protection against them.

The mine gases referred to are three in number—black-damp, fire-damp and white-damp. Until about the middle of the seventeenth century—that is, about four centuries after mining in Scotland began —black-damp was the only one of the three that presented danger. Prior to this time the workings were so shallow that fire-damp does not appear to have been encountered in dangerous quantities, a fortunate circumstance having regard to the explosive nature of fire-damp when mixed with air in certain proportions.

Black-damp, a non-poisonous and non-inflammable gas, usually consisting of nitrogen, oxygen and a small but varying proportion of carbon dioxide, is produced by the oxidation of certain mineral substances found in the coal and in the surrounding strata. As a result of this chemical action some of the oxygen in the mine air is used up, and unless the oxygen is replenished the miner runs the risk of asphyxiation. In earlier times, the miner endeavoured to " beat out the gas " with his jacket, or by any other handy means available, under the belief he would thereby induce fresh air currents to enter the workings.

Another method of getting rid of black-damp was to light a fire underground, especially near the bottom of the shaft or opening to the surface, whereby the warm air would rise, causing an air current to circulate which would carry the black-damp with it to the surface. This was known as furnace ventilation, a modified version of which was still in use in the early years of this century. (Fig. 16, p. 65).

With the passage of time, the shallower and more accessible seams of coal became exhausted and the working depths of collieries steadily increased, so that by about the middle of the seventeenth century depths of 200 feet or even more were not uncommon. It was at this point that a new gas menace, much more formidable than black-damp, began to appear. The name given to this new gas was fire-damp—on account of its highly inflammable and explosive nature. The great majority of the all-too-frequent fires and explosions described in contemporary reports of mining disasters were almost certainly started by the accidental ignition of fire-damp, now being encountered in increasing volume as mining operations become deeper and more extensive.

The alarm created by the increasing quantities of fire-damp in the mines resulted in the introduction of various devices such as fire baskets, air ducts, and other ventilation measures of uncertain efficiency. For almost three centuries the practice of " firing the gas " was also employed to get rid of fire-damp, miners specially chosen for this work being termed " firemen ". The men, after soaking their clothing in water, entered the working places with a lighted candle or torch and burned off the fire-damp to allow the miners to work in safety. Such a hazardous undertaking called for no inconsiderable degree of courage, though it appears to have been regarded as just part of the day's work.

As deeper mines were constructed and the fire-damp menace increased, some pits were provided with twin shafts or outlets. The twin-shaft system which began about the end of the sixteenth or the beginning of the seventeenth century—although not made compulsory until 1862—resulted in a definite improvement in ventilation standards. Consequently, as more pits of this type were constructed it became possible to make a much wider study of pit ventilation principles generally.

Fire-damp, the term used in mining for methane or marsh gas is the carburetted hydrogen (CH_4) evolved from the decay of buried vegetation, and is produced by the same chemical processes as those which formed coal itself. As more and more methane formed it became adsorbed in the coal seam and surrounding strata, where it often remained trapped under pressure (as much as thirty atmospheres having been recorded) until ultimately released during mining operations. That it did not noticeably impede operations during the early centuries of mining may be attributed to the methane in the shallower seams having escaped to the surface before mining operations commenced.

One of the earliest references to fire-damp appeared in a paper read to the then recently formed Royal Society in the reign of Charles II. At that time, miners and men of learning all appear to have been equally mystified by the emergence of this new danger, the " Vapour " at that time being regarded as some sort of subterranean demon whose " breath " destroyed men in an instant. In Scotland, the common belief during the Middle Ages was that the Deil himself sent this foul vapour into the mine to destroy any who sought to invade his realms!

Fire-damp is colourless, usually odourless, and being lighter than air is found near the roof. When the proportion present in the mine air reaches 5 per cent. an inflammable and dangerous mixture is formed. As the percentage of fire-damp increases explosibility also increases, until at about 9 per cent. the mixture is at "maximum explosibility". As more fire-damp is added, this explosive condition reduces until the proportion of fire-damp in the mixture reaches 15 per cent., when the danger of explosion disappears. In the interests of safety, the rule laid down is that men must be withdrawn when the methane present in the mine air exceeds 2 per cent (see Plate 23, facing page 97).

A third gas, white-damp, must now be mentioned. This gas is better known to chemistry students as carbon monoxide (CO). Carbon monoxide, which is deadly poisonous, is formed when carbon burns in a restricted quantity of air: it burns in oxygen to form CO_2. Dangerously large quantities of CO often appear in the mixture of gases left after an explosion, a mixture usually called " after-damp ". The amount of CO usually present in after-damp has often been responsible for far more deaths than the explosion itself. Being colourless and practically odourless its presence is difficult to detect, and some small warm-blooded creature such as a canary or a mouse is usually employed to give warning when CO is about, as these animals react more quickly than humans. CO has a strong affinity for the haemoglobin in the blood, with which it combines readily to form a compound called carboxy-haemoglobin. When this happens the blood loses its oxygen-carrying capacity and the victim will be suffocated unless speedily removed. Special breathing apparatus is now available, however, which enables miners and rescuers to work safely in the gas.

The avoidance of explosions may be regarded as one of the prime objectives of the safety code; the most effective way of dealing with this danger is by maintaining a high standard of ventilation at all times throughout the mine, and thereby preventing the formation of a dangerous concentration of gas.

THE MINER'S LAMP AND ATTENDANT DANGERS

It had long been known that the light by which the miner worked, however hard he tried to make it safe, was largely responsible for setting off many of the terrible explosions which occurred underground, and by the latter half of the eighteenth century, scientists and mining engineers were endeavouring to provide a really safe lamp. The problem was to discover some means by which the entrance of air and the exit of the waste gases could be regulated to allow the lamp to function normally without the risk of the flame escaping from the lamp and causing the mine gases outside to ignite or explode. Such a lamp was at last discovered, the three names associated chiefly with this historic discovery being Dr Clanny, George Stephenson and Sir Humphry Davy.

The principles of the construction of the safety lamp were known to both Dr Clanny and George Stephenson some years before Sir Humphry Davy (in 1815) hit upon the seemingly simple but quite brilliant idea of surrounding the flame of the lamp with a cylinder of wire gauze of suitable mesh. The perforations in the gauze allowed air to enter to enable the lamp to burn; at the same time, the gauze formed an effective barrier preventing the flame of the lamp reaching and igniting the inflammable gases (if any) present in the mine air

PLATE 21—SAFETY. Trainee being instructed in prop setting.

PLATE 22—Some early types of miners' lamps.

PLATE 23—SHOTFIRING. Miner testing for gas holding lamp close to roof.

PLATE 24—SHOTFIRING. Miner using an electrical drill prior to shotfiring.

outside, due to the heat of the flame being absorbed and conducted away by the gauze.

It is interesting to note that not one of these three inventors sought to patent his own particular lamp, though each had several prototypes to his credit. Their sole object had been to serve the cause of humanity, not seeking any pecuniary advantage for themselves.

Despite the protection afforded by the new safety lamp, many serious fires and explosions continued to occur during the years that followed, it being said that many colliery owners were now emboldened to work gassy seams that had previously been considered too dangerous without paying sufficient attention to ventilation and other safety precautions. Between 1835 and 1850 over six hundred fires and explosions in British mines were reported. During this time naked lights and candles were still being used, even in fiery mines, because of their greater illumination. The Davy lamp was subsequently found to be unreliable in high velocity air currents, and was later superseded by such improved versions as the Gray, Marsaut, Evan Thomas and Muesseler safety flame lamps. For general use these, in turn, gave way to still more efficient flame safety lamps, and then to the miner's electric safety lamp of to-day.

MINE DUST

The part played in recurring mining disasters by coal dust was for a long time unsuspected. Professor Faraday and Lyell drew attention to the matter in 1844. Later, William Galloway, who had begun to form certain conclusions of his own when acting as a Junior Inspector of Mines at Cardiff, demonstrated before the Royal Society the disastrous extent to which coal dust can extend an explosion of gas. His views and conclusions, however, aroused so much hostility at the time that he was obliged to resign his appointment! A Royal Commission Report in 1893 confirmed Galloway's theory, one result of which was the placing of certain restrictions on the use of explosives. As a further precaution against coal dust explosions, the use of water sprays was strongly advocated to prevent coal dust becoming airborne.

Further investigations undertaken by Galloway, Atkinson, Garforth, Haldane and others in the 1890's resulted in the discovery of a new (and most important) way of preventing coal dust explosions. It had been observed that certain coal dusts were much less liable to explode than others and it was thought this had some association with the amount of stone dust present in the coal dust. Stringent tests were carried out showing that when stone dust is spread on the coal dust in suitable proportions it became almost impossible to explode the resulting mixture, and so at last one of the main causes underlying the more violent types of explosion was finally solved. In stone dusting, the general practice is to use limestone, which can be applied without danger to the miners' health.

OTHER HAZARDS

Considerable space has been devoted to dangers arising from mine gases and dusts. But these are by no means the only dangers to be considered. Falls of ground are still responsible for far more accidents and a much greater loss of life than explosions, and a considerable effort is being made to improve timbering and support techniques, special attention being paid to the use of hydraulic and friction props, which enable the miner to support his roof more firmly and securely and enable him, also, to withdraw his supports more easily and safely.

The number of accidents from falls of ground has dropped appreciably in recent times, and could be reduced still further if the timbering and setting of supports were carried out with the care and attention such a vital safety precaution demands. The Coal Mines Act sets down certain minimum standards for controlling and supporting the roof, but the miner himself must decide what additional support he ought to set having regard to the particular roof conditions with which he is dealing for the moment. Bare compliance with the statutory regulations in this all-important matter is unwise.

Shotfiring is another operation that should always be performed with extreme care. Rules governing this subject are numerous and explicit, and since the first statutory references to shotfiring appeared in the Coal Mines Act of 1872 much study has been given to discovering the kind of explosive that may be safely used, and the best way to prepare a shot. One notable advance in shotfiring practice is the use of sheathed explosives in which an outer sheath of inert material surrounds the explosive so that when the explosive is fired the sheath releases and supplies an inert gas which so smothers or cools the flame that the risk of gas ignition is extremely remote. A still safer explosive has now been introduced, known as Eq.S. With this type of explosive the sheathing material is intimately mixed through the explosive.

SAFER UNDERGROUND TRANSPORT

The increasing use of non-inflammable conveyor belting and the introduction of locomotive haulage between the pit bottom and the end of the conveyor " run " have in recent times made a vital new contribution to safety in the mines. The danger of the conveyor belting catching fire as a result of frictional heating may now be considered to have almost disappeared. With the introduction of mine cars and locomotives, running on level roads, accidents from broken haulage ropes and runaway hutches are becoming fewer. The use of man-riding trains, too, greatly reduces the risks to which the men may be exposed while travelling to and from their working places. Another important safety factor is the introduction of machinery for the automatic loading of mine cars on the cages. This has eliminated many of the dangers to which onsetters and banksmen were formerly exposed when hutches had to be controlled and loaded on the cages by hand. The increasing use of power-loading methods, incorporating the use of prop-free fronts and caving, should help to make roof control operations easier and safer in future.

Flooding underground is rare by comparison with earlier experience. Special precautions must now be taken when approaching an area that is likely to contain water or other liquid material such as moss, while the construction of special lodgments to hold any temporary excess of mine water and the better pumping facilities at collieries have combined to reduce flooding dangers considerably.

With the increasing use underground of modern high-speed machinery for coal-getting and tunnel driving special measures are now in force to prevent stone or coal dust getting into the miners' lungs and injuring his health. The main approach to this problem is the straightforward one of using powerful sprays to lay the dust at source to prevent it from becoming airborne. Drilling and coal-cutting equipment and machinery are now fitted with strong water jets to check the emission of dust while water is also used copiously at other points where dust tends to be a pathological hazard such as at coal loading stations or transfer points on the underground haulage.

The Scientific Branch of the National Coal Board is responsible for the regular collection and analysis of samples of the mine air at all necessary points in order to ensure that the dust suppression measures installed are effective. Many miles of water pipes have had to be laid through colliery workings for this purpose. Water infusion of the seam is also practised. In this new method of controlling dust, water is forced into boreholes along the coalface under high pressure so that it flows into the small breaks and crevices in the seam, thus wetting any pre-formed dust in the coal seam before it is released by normal mining operations.

Medical officers attached to the industry and medical teams of specialists from outside the industry are regularly engaged in research into health problems arising from employment in the mines, while provision of medical centres at collieries and other health facilities has been extended considerably in recent years. Training in ambulance work, first aid, mine rescue, fire fighting, and in other safety and welfare activities is now firmly established as part of the National Coal Board's organisation for the promotion of the health, well-being and safety of the miner.

Over the past hundred years Health and Safety Regulations have been continually reviewed as fresh discoveries and further experience accumulated. It is not possible to make adequate acknowledgement to the various associations and bodies, public and private, which have taken part in this work, but mention may be made of The Institution of Mining Engineers, the first of whose constituent Institutes was formed in 1852; H.M. Inspectorate of Mines; and a much younger body, the Safety in Mines Research Board. All of these have made important contributions towards the development of the health and safety measures referred to in this Chapter.

The Trade Unions, Select and Departmental Committees, Royal Commissions, and many learned and representative bodies—all of which have contributed to the health and safety standards now firmly established—have earned the gratitude of the mineworker and of the industry generally.

In January, 1957, a new Coal Mines Act, revising and bringing up to date the Safety Code, came into force. In conclusion, the National Coal Board, who are now responsible for the efficient conduct of the industry, have set up a comprehensive Safety Organisation with trained full-time personnel at Colliery, Area, Divisional and National levels.

CHAPTER VIII

TYPES AND USES OF SCOTTISH COALS

AS EXPLAINED in an earlier part of this book, our coals represent the remains of a once prolific and varied land vegetation which flourished during what is known as the Carboniferous Period; vegetation which, in the course of many millions of years, has been altered, or metamorphosed, into the solid, black material we now use as a fuel. During this process of alteration only the more resistant portions of the original plants have been preserved—pieces of bark, fragments of woody tissue, parts of the framework or skin of leaves, the coverings of spores, etc. Differences in the kind and proportions of the original plant materials that accumulated in the old forests and forest-swamps have led to the formation of different types of coal.

Scotland possesses a number of different types, most of which belong to the category of what has long been known as bituminous coals. These show a banded structure, well seen in the alternating bright and dull layers present. The layers or bands of bright coal, sometimes referred to as clarain (Latin *clarus*, clear) are distinguished by their fine lamination and glossy lustre and often contain many relatively large fragments of plant tissue, etc. The layers or bands of dull coal, or durain, as it is called (Latin *durus*), are, on the other hand, hard, compact and non-reflecting. To the unaided eye they appear to be structureless, but thin sections examined under the microscope reveal much finely divided plant-material. Another common component of these banded coals is represented by the thin layers or streaks of a soft, black, sooty and powdery material known as fusain or "mineral charcoal", which often retains the cellular structure of plant tissues. It is fusain which so readily leaves a black mark on the fingers when handling coal. The proportions in which clarain, durain and fusain are present differ not only in different seams but also in different parts of the same seam.

Before dealing in some greater detail, however, with our bituminous coals, there is one other type which must be mentioned—cannel coal. Cannel coal is a tough, compact, uniform and non-laminated material, with a dull lustre and an irregular fracture. It consists

101

largely of very finely divided plant-debris, sometimes with scattered colonies of freshwater algae. It differs from ordinary coal in its mode of origin, having been formed over very limited areas in shallow sheets of water in which drifting plant-debris was constantly accumulating. It differs from ordinary coal also in sometimes containing animal remains (e.g., scales and teeth of fish). Cannel coals are local in their occurrence either as individual seams or as a component of ordinary coals. They are rich in volatile matter and burn with a long, bright flame. Cannel (a variant of candle) coal was at one time widely sought after as a source of illuminating gas (*see* p. 52). A special kind of cannel is the once well-known Torbanite or Boghead Gas Coal, worked for a few years near Bathgate in the middle of last century as a source of oil. Torbanite, largely composed of colonies of freshwater algae, yielded on distillation up to 120 gallons of crude oil per ton of raw material. It was the exhaustion of this seam that led to a search for a material to replace it and to the discovery of oil-shale in the Broxburn district about 1858.[1]

OUR BITUMINOUS COALS

It is upon the abundance, ease of access and variety of our bituminous coals that the industrial and economic development of Scotland during the past two hundred years has largely depended, and something must now be said regarding their characteristics, range of types, classification and uses.

The controlling factors in the production of the different varieties or types of bituminous coal have been:—

(1) Variations in the nature of the original plant material out of which the coals were formed;

(2) Differences in the changes to which this plant material was subjected either at the time of its formation or during its later geological history (*see* Chapter I, especially p. 25).

These two factors have combined to produce varieties or types of coal which differ widely in both their physical and chemical proper-

---

[1] Oil-shales, that is shales which yield crude oil on distillation in retorts, have been worked in the Lothians for over a hundred years. These shales occur at a much lower level in the succession of Carboniferous rocks than the workable coals. Typical Lothians oil-shale is a fine, dark-brown or almost black shale, tough and leathery in appearance and with a characteristic brown streak. It differs from ordinary shale (Scottish blaes) also in its resistance to disintegration by weathering and in the tendency of thin shavings or flakes to curl.

ties. Physical properties include such qualities as hardness, specific gravity, structure (e.g., variations in the thickness and distribution of the bands of bright and dull coal present), melting point, etc. The degree of hardness becomes of importance when coal has to be transhipped or transported for a distance. Some coals are mainly composed of bright layers and yield a fuel that burns freely with a bright flame until reduced to ashes. Others again are hard and dull coals which do not break readily and burn slowly and steadily away. Free-burning coals, for example, although excellent for household purposes would not be suitable in a ship as they would burn away too quickly and create steam-raising difficulties of a serious nature.

The differences in the behaviour of coal when heated is reflected also in the amount of volatile matter (gas, tar, etc.) given off and in the nature of the residual coke. The designation caking is given to coals which when heated in the absence of air yield a strong, porous, carbon-rich residue which can withstand pressure. These qualities are of great importance in the manufacture of iron in blast-furnaces and in other metallurgical processes, where a soft, non-coherent coke would tend to crush and so interfere with the free passage of air and hot gases through the furnace. From this particular point of view our coals may fall into the categories of non-caking, weakly-caking, medium-caking and strongly-caking.

All coals contain a variable amount of mineral matter or ash. This ash is derived in part from mineral matter present in the original plant debris out of which the coal was formed, in part from fine clay particles washed or blown in among the plant debris as it accumulated, and in some cases in part from deposits left by percolating mineral-bearing waters after the coal was formed.[1] The nature and amount of ash left after a coal is burnt is of great importance in certain industrial processes. For example, a highly fusible ash will tend to adhere closely to furnace bars and furnace linings, reducing the draught and leading to damage in its removal.

Coals also show wide differences in their chemical composition. A chemical analysis will show the relative amounts of fixed carbon, volatile matter, ash and moisture which a particular sample contains. It also provides information regarding the percentage of sulphur

[1] Films of light-coloured minerals, mainly carbonates of calcium and iron, are often found lining the surfaces of cracks or joints in coal and are collectively termed ankerite. Locally in some seams the carbonate content becomes so great as to produce what is known as "calcareous coal".

present,[1] the calorific value[2] and the caking properties. Alternatively, an analysis may show the composition expressed in elements—carbon, hydrogen, oxygen, sulphur, nitrogen, etc. Both methods of analysis yield valuable information but neither gives a complete picture of the character of the coal or of its behaviour under the different conditions encountered in industry. Much depends on its physical properties and these too must be taken into account in assessing its value for particular purposes.

Classification of Coals—It will be seen from what has been said in the preceding paragraphs that the problem of the classification of coals is a complex one. Classification of some sort is essential if each variety or type is to be used for the particular purpose for which it is best suited. But no system of classification can take into account *all* the variable and non-related factors—whether physical or chemical—which affect quality and ultimately industrial use. A simple classification may be based on content of volatile matter, as follows:

CLASS OF COAL	VOLATILE PERCENTAGE
1. Anthracite	Less than 9·1
2. Semi-anthracite	9·1 to 13·5
3. Semi-bituminous coals	13·6 to 19·5
4. Medium-volatile bituminous coals	19·6 to 32·0
5. High-volatile bituminous coals	Over 32

By far the largest proportion of Scottish coals fall into category 5 of the above table. This classification, however, gives no information regarding caking properties and little or no guidance as to suitability for a particular industry. Another classification that has been used is based upon the ratio existing between the amounts of carbon and hydrogen present in coals. The classification adopted by the National Coal Board is based essentially upon volatile content and upon the type of coke produced. The coke types are differentiated by means of a simple test which assigns to each a position in three main categories—weakly-caking, medium-caking or strongly-caking. The weakly-caking coals are used in the domestic market and for steam raising, the medium-caking in the gas industry, and the strongly-caking in the manufacture of metallurgical coke.

---

[1] Sulphur is a deleterious element in coals. Scottish coals possess the signal advantage of having, in general, a low sulphur content—rarely exceeding 1 per cent.

[2] The calorific value, or heating power, of a coal is generally expressed in British Thermal units, where the unit is the amount of heat required to raise 1 lb. of water 1 degree Fahrenheit. Alternatively, it can be expressed in calories, where the unit is the amount of heat required to raise a gramme of water 1 degree Centigrade.

Coal Carbonisation—When coal is heated in an oven or retort (with the air excluded) to a sufficiently high temperature the volatile constituents are given off in the form of crude coal gas, leaving a solid residue of coke. The coke may be hard or soft according to the degree of heat employed, the type of coal used, etc. The crude volatile products consist of two parts: (*a*) a non-condensible part containing a mixture of gases used for lighting or heating purposes, and (*b*) a condensible fraction yielding ammoniacal liquor, crude benzol and coal-tar. In the coke industry the primary product sought is coke,[1] the gas and tar being of secondary importance. In the gas industry, on the other hand, the order of importance is reversed; here gas is the main product,[2] with tar and coke as by-products. Both industries employ what is known as the High Temperature Carbonisation Process, although using different kinds of plant and heat treatment to obtain the particular product or products required with the least possible loss.

The by-products obtained by these carbonisation processes have become, mainly during the last fifty years, the basis of an immense industry built up on coal-tar derivatives. With by-product recovery now in general use, coal carbonisation is able to supply all the raw materials required for a wide range of industries. In addition to tar, other substances recovered for further treatment include ammoniacal liquor and crude benzol; and all three products can, by chemical treatment and redistillation, be further refined to give a vast number of chemical compounds.

The ammoniacal liquor is mainly used in the manufacture of nitrogenous fertilisers and as a source of ammonium nitrate in the explosives industry.

The crude benzol is refined to yield motor spirit, benzene, toluene, xylene and naphtha, which are in turn used in the manufacture of paints, varnishes, perfumery, plastics, and various medicinal products (see Chart on pp. 72/73).

From the heavy oils distilled from the tar come carbolic acid and other disinfectants, creosote oil for timber preservation and naphthalene and anthracene for the dye-stuff industries.

The pitch left as a residue after the extraction of the heavy oils is used to make carbon electrodes in the manufacture of aluminium,

---

[1] For the earliest use in Scotland of coal-coke to smelt iron ores see page 49.

[2] For the beginnings of the gas industry see page 52.

as an ingredient in fuel briquettes and in binding the materials used to surface public highways. M.M.

DISTRIBUTION OF COAL SUPPLIES[1]

By far the greater part of Scotland's output of coal is consumed within her own boundaries. At present annual output and annual home demand are running fairly close together, with the result that the exportable surplus is much smaller than it was before the war (*see* Table below). The broad trend of coal consumption being steadily upwards the Scottish Divisional Coal Board are endeavouring to expand the productive capacity of the Industry in order to meet the increased home requirements that are anticipated and to provide in addition an adequate surplus for coastwise and export shipment.

In the distribution of coal supplies two considerations must be kept in view: (*a*) the type of coal, and (*b*) the size of coal as it leaves the preparation plant. Both considerations are of extreme importance if the varied requirements of industry are to be adequately met. At present the Scottish production of individual types and sizes of coal in some cases falls short of, and in other cases exceeds, the home demand for these particular types and sizes. Hence, Scotland has to bring in from England or from abroad tonnages of such coals as are in short supply, while sending away tonnages of coals which are relatively more plentiful.

The following Table shows the amount of coal consumed by Scottish markets during 1936–38 (yearly average), 1947 and 1955, together with estimated figures of tonnages that may be required in 1965.

Coal Consumption in Scotland

MARKET	1936/38	1947	1955	1965 (estimate)
		Million tons		
Gas	1·86	2·29	2·43	2·00
Electricity	1·08	2·31	3·15	4·50
Railways	2·13	2·33	1·93	1·30
Coke Ovens	·91	1·30	1·63	3·00
Industry	6·70	6·94	6·96	6·00
Domestic	5·00	3·49	3·66	3·50
Colliery Consumption and Miners' Coal	2·50	2·05	1·68	1·00
	20·18	20·71	21·44	21·30

[1] Information supplied by the Marketing Department of the Scottish Division.

CHANGING DEMANDS OF INDUSTRY

Although the annual tonnage of coal moving from the collieries to industry is much the same as pre-war, the actual amounts distributed to individual markets show a number of significant changes. For example, the demand of industry for electricity and, to some extent, for gas has shown a marked increase and this in turn requires more coal. Keener competition in selling our manufactured goods in foreign markets makes modernisation of plant a necessity and this and other factors are resulting in an ever-increasing demand for power. Electricity from atomic power stations is not expected to be available in significant quantity for some years. While the hydro-electric schemes are playing an important part in providing electricity, it would appear that for the next decade at least we must rely on the steam stations using coal. Some of the modern steam stations producing electricity, such as that at Braehead in Renfrewshire, at present use as much as 2,500 tons of coal per day when working to capacity, while the new station being built at Kincardine-on-Forth will use, it is estimated, as much as 3,600 tons per day by 1961.

Increasing demands for coal are also being made by the iron and steel industry for use in their coke ovens. Vast quantities of steel have been required to support the post-war effort and the steel industry in Scotland is steadily expanding. To make steel requires pig iron from the blast-furnaces and these in turn require iron-ore and metallurgical coke. The latter is produced in coke ovens from coals with suitable coking properties, the process being known as carbonisation (see p. 105), and the same type of coal is also in strong demand by gas works. Scotland's reserves of these coking or "carbonisation" coals are, however, limited, although every effort is being made by the Scottish Division of the National Coal Board to increase available supplies.

Another illustration of changing conditions is the diminishing output of screened large coal in relation to total output. This is due partly to the fact that in general thinner seams are now being worked and partly to the introduction of mechanised mining which tends to break the coal into small sizes. This problem is perhaps particularly noticeable in the domestic market recently freed from rationing restrictions, where there is a definite shortage of suitable large coal. Traditionally, of course, households have long been accustomed to burn large coal in open fires, the efficiency of some of which was, and still is, very low. There are now available, however, a number of domestic purpose appliances for use with open or closed fires which are designed not only to burn the smaller sizes of coal, but also to give a much greater efficiency.

The question may be asked as to whether there is likely to be any immediate relaxation of the increasing demand for coal in Scotland. In this connection it may be noted that the gradual conversion of British Railways' locomotives to diesel oil firing will result in a saving of large coal. There is scope also for saving coal by increased efficiency of plant in many factories either by the improvement or by the replacement of existing plant, and the National Industrial Fuel Efficiency Service is engaged in giving consumers guidance in this matter. Conversion of coal-burning to oil-burning plant is another factor which reduces the demand for coal; there have been already a number of such conversions in Scotland, notably at iron and steel works. Nor should it be forgotten that both electricity stations and gas works are becoming progressively more efficient in the use of coal as old plant is replaced with modern plant.

Markets outside Scotland—That Scottish coal is in demand by consumers beyond the borders of Scotland is shown by the following Table.

Disposals to Markets outwith Scotland

	1936–38 (average)	1947	1955	1965 (estimate)
		Million tons		
Export Cargo and Foreign Bunkers	6·90	·95	1·37	2·00
England	2·80	·72	·37	2·00
Northern Ireland	1·30	·88	·84	2·00
	11·00	2·55	2·58	6·00

How soon Scotland will be able to resume exports on the pre-war scale shown in the Table is still a moot point, though every effort is being made to recover these markets.

Transporting the Coal to the Consumer—After the coal has been cleaned and graded at the collieries it is loaded into railway wagons. When weighed and ticketed, the wagons are then ready to start their journey either directly to the premises of the merchant or consumer who has bought the coal, or alternatively to the nearest railway station. From the collieries or starting points supplies have to be distributed to thousands of stations and private sidings throughout the length and breadth of the country, requiring a great deal of expert traffic organisation by the railway company. Each day thousands of full wagons of coal are in transit. Each wagon undergoes a sorting and re-sorting operation at one or other of the railway company's marshalling yards to enable wagons going in the same direction to be re-assembled and coupled up in readiness to complete their journey

Large consumers such as electricity stations, gas works and iron and steel works can take in complete train loads at a time, and where it is practical wagons are assembled into full train loads in the colliery's own sidings. This saves time and work in transit and much thought is given to extending this feature. Where trains cannot be arranged direct from one sending point to one destination, wagons from nearby pits are joined up at a convenient railway yard and moved forward to a similar concentration point serving adjacent destinations.

The most difficult points to supply are the local stations and mineral depots because these handle detailed consignments of all the various types of coal and the quantities involved vary considerably from week to week. Imagine trying to arrange the train, carrying different kinds of coal, so that as it comes to each local station on its route it can drop off the right wagon or wagons without having to shunt almost endlessly, and also lose precious running time.

Let us take an illustration. A Lothians colliery has twenty wagon loads standing ready, ten destined for Glasgow, one for Hawick, one for Galashiels and the other eight for local stations in the Edinburgh district. The engine driver will take all twenty of them to a central marshalling yard near Edinburgh. He then proceeds with his engine to another colliery and uplifts a further batch of wagons and takes them to the marshalling yard, and so on. When duly sorted the Hawick and Galashiels wagons will be in one siding along with wagons from other pits going in the same direction; the ten Glasgow trucks in another where the full train load for that city is being made up, and the remaining eight wagons will be attached to the appropriate local trains delivering to the various depots in the Edinburgh district.

In Scotland alone, thousands of wagons are needed to handle coal traffic, and in order to reduce the number, larger wagons are being built. In the earlier days wagons carried about 8 tons of coal; then 10-ton and 12-ton wagons were introduced. After the second world war 16-ton wagons became the standard, although in some parts of England 21-ton wagons had been in use for some time. Railway experts believe that a wagon which could carry $24\frac{1}{2}$ tons of coal would be the ideal size and that all new collieries, power stations, etc., should be constructed so that the larger and higher wagon can safely pass underneath overhead structures. Appliances for weighing and emptying the heavier wagons would also have to be installed.

Seaborne coal traffic is also an important feature. From Firth of Forth ports coal is carried by tramp steamers to various European countries, and by small coasters to destinations on the Thames and Medway where many industrial plants are specially sited to receive seaborne coal. From Clyde and Ayrshire ports regular coal shipments are made to Ireland, while extensive use is still made of a considerable fleet of small "puffers" which thread their way through sea loch and canal to innumerable and otherwise inaccessible points on the broken coastline of the Western Highlands and Islands. These shipping points can deal only with railborne coal. The British Transport Commission own a number of the principal docks, such as Ayr, Grangemouth and Methil. Glasgow Docks are owned and administered by the Clyde Navigation Trust, and Leith Docks by the Leith Dock Commission.

Although most of the coal is conveyed by rail for some part of its journey, a growing volume is now being carried by road. Most of this is for short local deliveries, but an increasing number of more distant consumers who do not have private railway sidings of their own, and who in the past had to have their coal sent to the nearest railway station for transfer to road vehicle, are finding it more convenient to have their coal sent direct from the pit to their premises by road.

INDEX

A

	PAGE
Abbey charters relating to early coal-workings	34, 35
Acknowledgments	16
After-damp	96
Age of Forests, the	17–23
Air in mines, amount entering and leaving, *see also* Ventilation . .	68
Anderton Shearer Loader	83
Anti-dust measures	99, 100
Ash in coal	103
Ayrshire, early workings in	35, 39
section across Mauchline Basin	31
workable coals in	32

B

BAIRD, William, & Co. Ltd.	75
BALD, Robert	48, 50
Bearers in early coal mines	37, 40, 58, 68
Bell-pits	37, 38
Bituminous coals, types of	100–104
Blackband Ironstone	54
Black-damp	93–94
Blast furnaces	15, 48, 49, 54
Bloomeries	48
BOECE, Hector	39
Boghead Gas Coal	102
Bo'ness, early coal-workings near	34, 39
Boring for coal	23, 32, 51, 62–63
Boulder clay	29
Brora, coal at	28, 30, 39
BRUCE, Sir George	42
Burn Pit, Kinneil	48, 80

C

Caking coals	103, 104, 107
Calamites	12, 17, 21
Calorific value of coals	104
Campsie Hills	25
Cannel coal	52, 101–102
Canonbie coalfield	30
Carbon-content in coals	103–104
Carboniferous Period	23–26
Carboniferous rocks, types of	23, 25
thickness of	25
sub-divisions of	25, 29, 30
folding and faulting of	26, 31
invaded by dykes and sills	26–27
buried under later formations	27–28
re-exposed by denudation	28
Carbonisation of coals, products of	105–106
See also pp. 72–73	
Carriden	34
Carron Ironworks	49
Central Coalfield	32
Changing demands of industry	107–108
Clackmannanshire	33, 39
Clanny Safety Lamp	96

Clarain 101
Clayband Ironstone 49
Clyde, River 46, 50
Clydeside, industrialisation of 50, 61, 68
Coal, origin of 17–23
    stages in the formation of 25–26
Coal and Iron Age 50–54
Coal carbonisation, products of 105–106
    See also pp. 72–73
Coal consumption in recent years 106
Coal conveyors 71, 74
Coal cutters 74–76, 81–82
Coal dust, danger from 89–90, 97–98
Coal gas 15, 52, 102, 103, 105
    See also pp. 72–73
Coal in early times, prejudice against use of 14, 35
Coal plough 83
Coal preparation plant 87, 88, 106
Coal tar 52, 72–73, 103, 105
Coals and coalfields of Scotland: distribution and general structure of
    coalfields 29–32
        number of workable seams 32
        reserves of coal 32–33
        types and uses of coals 101–106
COCKBURN, Henry 60
Coke 15, 48, 49, 52, 73, 103, 105, 107
Colliery development: new sinkings and reconstructions . . 86, 87, 88
Compressed air as a source of power . . . 80, 81–82, 83
Conditions of life and work in early Scottish mines . . . 55–60
Cotton mills 50
Crossraguel Abbey 35
Culross 42
CUNNINGHAM, Sir George 44

D

Dailly 35
Davy Safety Lamp 96, 97
DAVY, Sir Humphry 92, 93
Day-levels 37, 38, 40, 44
Direct rope haulage 69, 70
Distribution of coal supplies 106–110
Drainage of mines, early methods used for . . 36, 37, 38, 42, 44, 46–47
    steam power used for 48, 51, 61
    development of pumping techniques . . . 76–77, 99
Drift deposits 29
Drift mines 86
Drilling for coal. *See* Boring.
Dunfermline Abbey 35, 40
Durain in coal 101
Dust in mines. *See under* Coal dust *and* Stone dust.
Dykes 26

E

Earth-pressures 26, 89
Earliest records of coal-workings 34–35
Earnock Colliery, Hamilton 82
East Lothian 32, 39
East Fife 39
    horizontal section across 31

PAGE

East Sutherland 30, 39
Edmonstone Colliery, Midlothian 45
Electricity: applied to mining problems 77, 79, 80, 84
    steam stations producing 82–83, 84, 107
Elphinstone Colliery, Airth 45
Endless rope haulage 71

F

FARADAY, Michael 82, 83, 97
Faults 22, 27
Fife 32, 33, 39, 44
Fireclays 25
"Fire-engine" 44–45
Fire-damp 47, 80, 89
Fire-places, introduction of 14
F.L.P. (flameproof) equipment 82, 83
Folding of the Carboniferous rocks 26, 27
Forest-swamps of Carboniferous times . . . . . 17–23 *passim*
Forth and Clyde Canal 49
Fossil Grove, Whiteinch, Glasgow 12, 19
Furnace Ventilation 43, 66, 94
Fusain in coal 101

G

GALLOWAY, William 97
Garleton Hills 25
Gartsherrie coal-cutter 75, 76, 81
Gas from distillation of coal 15, 52, 102, 103, 105
    See also pp. 72–73
Gases in coal-mines 47, 89, 90, 91, 93–96
Geological history of the coalfields 26–29
Geological Periods 28
Glacial Period 28–29
Glasgow 19, 44, 46, 50, 52
Govan Colliery 81

H

Haulage (underground), methods of, *see especially* . . 68–71, 72, 80, 87
Highlands 49
Holyrood Abbey 34
Horizon mining, layout 64
Horse-gins 40, 42, 43
Hydraulic transportation of coal to surface 79
Hydro-electric schemes 107

I

Ice Age 28–29
Industrial Revolution, the 15, 52, 61
"Ingaun e'es" 36
Inspectorate of Mines 91–92, 100
Iron Industry, rise of 15, 48–49
Iron ore, output figures 54
    types of, *see under* Blackband *and* Clayband.

113

J

	PAGE
Jacobite risings	46, 49
Jurassic Period	28, 30

K

Kilpatrick Hills	25
Kinneil	48
Kintyre, coal in	30, 39
Koepe system of winding	78, 79

L

Lanarkshire	53
Lepidodendron	12, 17
Limestone, burnt for agricultural use	51
Limestone Coal Group	30, 31, 32
Limestones	23, 25, 51
Lothians	36

See also under East, Mid *and* West Lothian.

M

MACADAM, J. Loudon	49, 52
Machine mining of coal	74–76
Machrihanish Coalfield	30
MACINTOSH, Charles	52
Main and tail rope haulage	70, 71
Man-riding trains	99
Mechanical conveyors	64, 71, 74
Medical services	88, 100
Methane gas. See Fire-damp.	
Midlothian Basin	30, 39
horizontal section across	31
workable coals in	32
Mine dust	97–100
Miner's lamp, development of	96–97
Mining, continuous principle	83
Mining hazards	89–100
Moat Pit, Culross	42
Monkland Canal	49, 53
Monktonhall Colliery	30
Muirkirk	32
MURDOCH, W.	52
MUSHET, R. F.	75

N

Nationalisation of the Coal Industry	85–88
Newbattle Abbey	34, 35, 39, 40
Newcomen engine	45, 47, 76
NEILSON, J.	54

O

Oil-shale	102
Opencast working of coal	24, 29
See also pp. 13, 36, 37.	
Output of coal, references to	14, 15, 36, 39, 42, 53, 54, 57, 86

114

P

	PAGE
Paisley Abbey	35
Permian Period	27–28
Physical properties of coal	103
Pig iron	48, 54
Pit-and-Adit system of working coal	13, 37, 38, 40
Pitch	53, 105–106
Pittencrieff	35
Population of Scotland, references to	14, 40, 57
Port Glasgow	46
Power, sources of. *See under* Compressed Air, Electricity *and* Steam.	
Power loading machines and techniques	83, 84, 99
Prestongrange	34, 39, 40
Prestonpans	35
Productive Coal Measures	30, 31, 32, 33
Pumping techniques, development of	76–77

R

Railway Age	15, 53
Reconstruction of collieries	33, 86, 87
Renfrewshire	25
Roads: conditions in early times	14, 35, 39, 46
improvements in	49, 52–53
Roof control in workings	36, 89, 98, 99
Royal Scottish Museum	75

S

Safety legislation, outstanding Acts	90, 91, 92
Safety precautions in mines, development of	89–100
Saline Hills	25
Salt and salt-pans	14, 35, 42
Saltcoats	44
Salters, status of	56, 58, 59, 60
Salters' Road, the	39
Sands and gravels, glacial	29
Sandstones	23, 25
Sanquhar	32
Savery Pump	76, 80
Scottish Division, National Coal Board	85, 106, 107
Seaborne coal traffic	110
Sea-coal	13, 35
Seed-ferns	17
Self-acting incline, use of	68, 69
Shafts: construction of modern	63–64, 87
limited depths in early times	37, 40, 42, 46, 48, 57
twin-shaft system introduced	42, 94
Shales	23, 25
Shotfiring	98–99
Skip system of winding	78, 79
Sills of igneous rock	26
Stage-coach	49, 53
Stair-pits	37, 41, 58
Steam-engine	15, 44–45, 47–48, 69
Steam power, applied to mining, *see* previous item *and* 51, 61, 69, 76–77, 80–81	
STEPHENSON, George	53, 69, 80, 90
Stone dust in mines	98, 99
Sulphur in coal	104
Surface drift mines	86

115

T

PAGE

Tar	52, 105
TELFORD, Thomas	49, 52, 53
Temperature increase in collieries	67
Torbanite	102
Tranent	34, 53
Transport of coal: in early times	14, 39, 46, 49
to-day	108–110
underground	64, 68–71, 74
Treaty of Union	40, 46
Trepanner	83
Turnpike roads	49
Types and uses of Scottish coals	101–106

U

Underground transport of coal	64, 68–71, 74

V

Ventilation of mines: early difficulties in	37, 42–43, 47, 52
later developments in the practice of	64–68, 94, 95

W

WADE, General	49
Wagonways	53
Water in mines. *See references under* Drainage.	
Water-gin	42, 43, 44
WATT, James	15, 47–48, 52, 76, 77, 80, 83
West Lothian	39
White-damp	93, 95
Winding coal, developments in	77–79, 84
See also pp. 87, 88.	
Winding, fully automatic	83, 84
Wire ropes, introduced	77, 79
Women and children in mines	15, 55–60 *passim*, 68
See also under Bearers.	
Wood, gradually replaced by coal as a domestic fuel	14, 39
Wood-charcoal	48, 49